LIBRARY, R.A.E., WESTCOTT

REGULATIONS FOR BORROWERS

1. Books are issued on loan for a period of 1 month and must be returned to the Library promptly.

2. Before books are taken from the Library receipts for them must be filled in, signed, and handed to a member of the Library Staff. Receipts for books received through the internal post must be signed and returned to the Library immediately.

3. Readers are responsible for books which they have borrowed, and are required to replace any such books which they lose. In their own interest they are advised not to pass on to other readers books they have borrowed.

4. To enable the Library Staff to deal with urgent requests for books, borrowers who expect to be absent for more than a week are requested either to arrange for borrowed books to be made available to the P.A. or Clerk to the Section, or to return them to the Library for safekeeping during the period of absence.

AGARDograph No. 7

INTRODUCTION TO THE STUDY OF CHEMICAL REACTIONS IN FLOW SYSTEMS

TO
MY WIFE

INTRODUCTION TO THE STUDY OF CHEMICAL REACTIONS IN FLOW SYSTEMS

By

S. S. PENNER

Daniel and Florence Guggenheim
Jet Propulsion Center,
California Institute of Technology,
Pasadena, California

Published for and on behalf of
THE ADVISORY GROUP FOR
AERONAUTICAL RESEARCH AND DEVELOPMENT
NORTH ATLANTIC TREATY ORGANIZATION
by
BUTTERWORTHS SCIENTIFIC PUBLICATIONS
LONDON
1955

BUTTERWORTHS PUBLICATIONS LTD.
88 KINGSWAY, LONDON, W.C.2

AFRICA: BUTTERWORTH & CO. (AFRICA) LTD.
DURBAN: 33/35 Beach Grove

AUSTRALIA: BUTTERWORTH & CO. (AUSTRALIA) LTD.
SYDNEY: 8 O'Connell Street
MELBOURNE: 430 Bourke Street
BRISBANE: 240 Queen Street

CANADA: BUTTERWORTH & CO. (CANADA) LTD.
TORONTO: 1367 Danforth Avenue

NEW ZEALAND: BUTTERWORTH & CO. (AUSTRALIA) LTD.
WELLINGTON: 49/51 Ballance Street
AUCKLAND: 35 High Street

Set in Monotype Baskerville type
Made and printed in Great Britain by
William Clowes and Sons, Limited, London and Beccles

CONTENTS

LIST OF ILLUSTRATIONS

ACKNOWLEDGEMENT

The author is happy to express his sincere appreciation to the Air Research and Development Command, United States Air Force, under whose sponsorship the present work was prepared. The work was performed under Contract AF18(600)–972.

S. S. PENNER

INTRODUCTION

THE present discussion is intended as an introduction to the study of chemical reactions in moving ideal gas mixtures. It is hoped that it will serve two distinct aims, namely, (1) to present an adequate summary of the principles of classical chemical kinetics, which is intelligible to investigators without previous training in chemical kinetics; (2) to provide the necessary basic material for intelligent formulation of flow problems with chemical reactions. The manuscript is divided into four chapters.

Chapter 1 contains a résumé of classical chemical kinetics with special reference to the limitations of the steady-state approximation for chain reactions. The material of Chapter 1 should serve as an introduction to the vast literature on chemical kinetics to which reference must be made for specific reaction-rate constants which are required for the phenomenological description of chemical reaction rates.

Chapter 2 contains a brief summary of the conservation laws for reacting fluids and suitable expressions for the determination of transport coefficients.

As a simple example of chemical reactions in flow systems, we analyze in Chapter 3 the problem of chemical reactions during adiabatic flow through a de Laval nozzle, which is a flow problem with negligible diffusion.

In Chapter 4 we consider the important problem of heterogeneous chemical reactions. After a brief discussion of stationary, isothermal, gas-solid systems, some of the important features of heterogeneous diffusion flames are considered.

The topics discussed in the present review are treated in textbooks or publications on chemical kinetics, combustion, fluid mechanics and applied physics. This wide spread of information may serve to emphasize the need for close collaboration between investigators trained in divergent scientific disciplines if the science of the dynamics of reacting fluids is to be carried to the point where it can become a useful tool for further technological development.

The author takes pleasure in expressing his sincere gratitude to Dr. Theodore von Kármán for critical comments and suggestions, without which this monograph could not have been written. The author is also indebted to Dr. H. S. Tsien for helpful critical remarks.

CHAPTER 1

CLASSICAL CHEMICAL KINETICS (PHENOMENOLOGICAL DESCRIPTION OF REACTION RATES IN STATIONARY, ISOTHERMAL SYSTEMS)

1.1. Formal Rate Law and Definitions

For the concentration of the chemical compound represented by the symbol M_i the chemist uses the following equivalent notations: (M_i), $[M_i]$, c_{M_i}; for the sake of uniformity we shall use (M_i) throughout Chapter 1. The unit of concentration will be chosen as the mole per cm^3, although the mole per liter is also employed frequently. The stoichiometric relation describing a one-step chemical reaction of arbitrary complexity may be represented by the equation

$$\sum_{j=1}^{n} \nu_j' \, M_j \rightarrow \sum_{j=1}^{n} \nu_j'' \, M_i \qquad \text{.... (1.1)}$$

where the ν_j' are the stoichiometric coefficients for the reactants, the ν_j'' represent corresponding coefficients for the reaction products, and the total number of chemical compounds involved is n. If the chemical species represented by (M_i) does not occur as reactant, then $\nu_i' = 0$, etc.

The meaning of Eq. 1.1 may be illustrated for the reaction between two hydrogen atoms in the presence of a third hydrogen atom to form a hydrogen molecule and a hydrogen atom which has gained (translational) energy. Symbolically we write

$$H + H + H \rightarrow H_2 + H$$

or

$$3H \rightarrow H_2 + H \qquad \text{.... (1.2)}$$

Here $n = 2$, $M_1 = H$, $M_2 = H_2$, $\nu_1' = 3$, $\nu_1'' = 1$, $\nu_2' = 0$, and $\nu_2'' = 1$. Note that, in the present notation, no distinction is made between hydrogen atoms having different energies. Again consider the overall chemical reaction between hydrogen and oxygen to form water:

$$2H_2 + O_2 \rightarrow 2H_2O \qquad \text{.... (1.3)}$$

Here $n = 3$, $M_1 = H_2$, $M_2 = O_2$, $M_3 = H_2O$, $\nu_1' = 2$, $\nu_2' = 1$, $\nu_3' = 0$, $\nu_1'' = \nu_2'' = 0$, $\nu_3'' = 2$. More complicated examples in which the ν_j' and ν_j'' are not necessarily integers can be given without difficulty. It is clear, however, that Eq. 1.1 is adequate to describe all possible chemical reactions.

According to the *law of mass action** the rate of disappearance of a chemical species is proportional to the products of the concentrations of the reacting chemical species, each concentration being raised to a power equal to the corresponding stoichiometric coefficient. Thus

$$\text{reaction rate} = k_f \prod_{j=1}^{n} (M_j)^{\nu_j'} \qquad .... \; (1.4)$$

where the proportionally constant k_f is called the *specific reaction-rate constant* or *coefficient*. A relation of the form of Eq. 1.4 was originally introduced as a postulate for reaction rates in homogeneous, static, and isothermal systems, i.e., for systems without temperature, concentration, pressure, or velocity gradients. For a given chemical reaction, the specific reaction rate constant k_f is independent of the concentrations (M_j) and depends only on the temperature. In general, k_f is given by an expression of the form

$$k_f = BT^{\alpha} \exp(-E/RT)$$

where the *frequency factor* B, the quantity α, and the *activation energy* E are parameters which are determined by the nature of the elementary reaction processes. For given chemical changes, these parameters are neither functions of the concentrations nor of the temperature. Throughout the following discussion it will be sufficient to regard k_f as an empirically determined coefficient which depends only on the temperature. A more detailed description of the nature of k_f and of its dependence on elementary processes is deferred to Sec. 1.6.

We shall always use k_i to denote a reaction-rate constant and shall employ frequently the subscript f to identify a forward reaction, i.e., a reaction in which the reactants appear on the left-hand side of the equation and the reaction products on the right-hand side of the equation.

The only observable results of a chemical reaction are net rates of change for the chemical components. It is clear from Eq. 1.1 that the net rate of production of M_i is

$$(\dot{M}_i) = \mathrm{d}(M_i)/\mathrm{d}t = (\nu_i'' - \nu_i') \text{ (reaction rate)}$$

$$= (\nu_i'' - \nu_i') k_f \prod_{j=1}^{n} (M_j)^{\nu_j'} \qquad .... \; (1.5)$$

since ν_i'' moles of M_i are formed for every ν_i' moles of M_i used up.

Application of Eq. 1.5 to reaction 1.2 leads to the result

$$(\dot{\mathrm{H}}) = -2(\dot{\mathrm{H}}_2) = -2k_f(\mathrm{H})^3$$

where the dot denotes a time derivative.

* The origin of the law of mass action and its relation to first principles are discussed in Sec. 1.6.

The process represented by Eq. 1.1 is said to be of order ν_j' with respect to M_j. The *overall order* of the reaction is said to be

$$m = \sum_{j=1}^{n} \nu_j'$$

Thus, reaction 1.2 is of the third order with respect to H, of zeroth order with respect to H_2; the reaction 1.2 is a third order (overall) reaction.

The hypothetical chemical reaction described by Eq. 1.3 represents a third-order process which is of second order with respect to H_2 and of first order with respect to O_2. Equation 1.3 is an example of a valid overall chemical reaction which does not describe correctly the reaction mechanism. Thus, the overall result for reaction between two moles of H_2 and one mole of O_2 is the production of two moles of H_2O; however, the conversion of H_2 and O_2 occurs by means of a series of successive, interdependent, elementary chemical reaction steps. For this reason, the rate expression obtained by applying Eq. 1.5 to Eq. 1.3, viz.,

$$(\dot{H}_2) = -(H_2\dot{O}) = 2(\dot{O}_2) = -2k_f(H_2)^2(O_2)$$

has no physical significance. The law of mass action, as expressed by Eq. 1.5, may be applied, in a meaningful way, only to elementary reaction steps which describe the correct reaction mechanism. For a number of simple chemical processes, a plausible reaction mechanism has been deduced by chemical kineticists; for some technically important reactions, chemical kineticists provide intelligent conjectures regarding the probable reaction mechanism. Detailed studies[1] show that the production of H_2O from H_2 and O_2 involves, among others, the following elementary reaction steps

$$OH + H_2 \rightarrow H_2O + H$$
$$H + O_2 \rightarrow OH + O$$

to each of which the law of mass action applies. The phenomenological description of interdependent chemical reactions is discussed in Sec. 1.4 and 1.5.

The stoichiometric coefficients for elementary reactions give information about the number of moles reacting, not about the weights or volumes which are changing. If the cubic centimeter (cm^3) is chosen as the unit of volume, it is apparent that the units of the rate constant k_f are

$$\frac{\text{moles}}{(\text{cm})^3\ \text{sec}}\ \frac{1}{(\text{moles/cm}^3)^m} = (\text{moles})^{1-m}\ (\text{cm}^3)^{m-1}\ \text{sec}^{-1}.$$

Thus, for a first order reaction, k_f is a frequency.

Chemical reaction rates are determined experimentally by studying, either directly or indirectly, the rate of change of concentration of reactants and/or of products with time. Experimental studies designed to determine reaction rates and mechanism are generally carried out in *static systems* under *isothermal conditions*. As a function of time, the concentrations of reactants will decrease asymptotically toward a limiting value (not necessarily zero) whereas the concentrations of product species will increase asymptotically toward a limiting value (cf. *Fig. 1.1*). For complex chemical reactions the slope of the concentration versus time curves may change sign repeatedly.

Experimental chemical kinetics is a science of considerable complexity because very large observable effects are frequently produced by uncontrolled factors such as minute concentrations of impurities, surface effects, photochemical changes brought about by stray light, etc. The absolute precision of even the best-known rate constants is low. The temperature dependence of k_f is such that extremely precise values of E are required to yield a reliable prediction for the change of k_f with temperature. Since observational data on k_f are restricted to a narrow temperature range, in which the observed results can be fitted equally

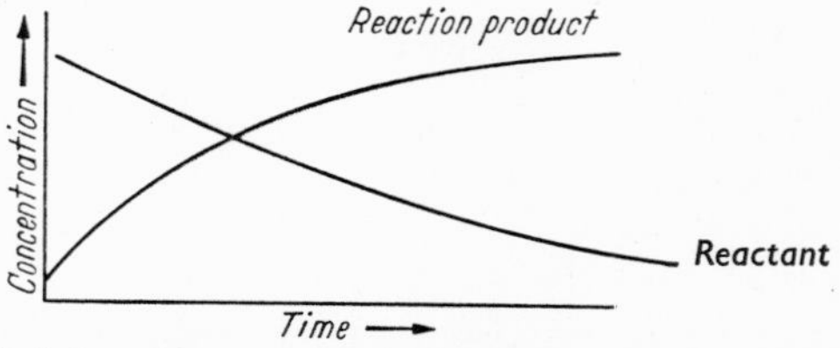

Fig. 1.1. Variation of concentrations of products and reactants with time (schematic).

well by a number of different rate laws, predictions of absolute values for k_f at elevated temperatures are almost always uncertain by an order of magnitude or more.

1.2. One-Step Chemical Reactions of Various Orders

(*A*) *First-order processes*

The rate law for the first-order process

$$A \rightarrow B \qquad .... (1.6)$$

is

$$(\dot{A}) = -(\dot{B}) = -k_f(A) \qquad .... (1.6a)$$

The rate expression given in Eq. 1.6a applies formally also to the process

$$A + C \rightarrow D, \ (C) \gg (A) \qquad .... (1.7)$$

Since (C) $\gg$ (A), the expression

$$(\dot{A}) = -(\dot{D}) = -k_f\,(A)\,(C)$$

becomes, for all practical purposes,

$$(\dot{A}) = -(\dot{D}) = k_f'(A), \ k_f' = k\ (C) = \text{constant.}$$

The process 1.6 is a unimolecular reaction which obeys first-order kinetics; the process 1.7 is a bimolecular reaction which obeys first-order kinetics and, therefore, illustrates the tenuous relation between molecularity and reaction mechanism, on the one hand, and empirically observed order of the reaction, on the other hand.

An example of an actual chemical process described by Eq. 1.6 is the following molecular rearrangement[2]

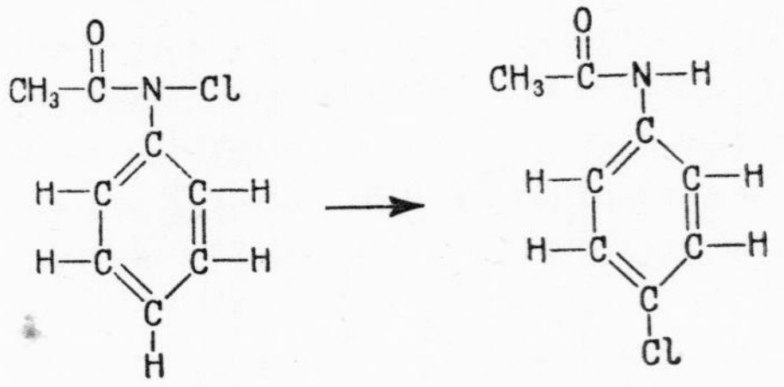

(N-*chloro-acetanilide*) (p-*chloro-acetanilide*)

The hydrolysis of sucrose in excess water,

$$C_{12}H_{22}O_{11} + H_2O \rightarrow 2C_6H_{12}O_6$$

(sucrose) (glucose + dextrose)

corresponds to Eq. 1.7.

Examples of complex reactions obeying first-order kinetics rate laws are the decomposition[3,4] of N_2O_5,

$$N_2O_5 \rightarrow N_2O_4 \text{ (or } 2NO_2) + (1/2)O_2$$

the thermal decomposition of azomethane[5],

$$C_2H_6N_2 \rightarrow C_2H_6 + N_2$$

(azomethane)

and the thermal decomposition of many hydrocarbons[6].

(*B*) *Second-order processes*

Most chemical reactions are bimolecular and proceed as the result of reactions following binary collisions. For this reason it is not surprising to note that chemical reactions frequently follow second-order kinetics. In complex processes, second-order kinetics may be considered as an indication that one of the bimolecular processes constitutes the *slow* or *rate-determining step*.

For the second-order bimolecular reaction

$$A + B \rightarrow C + D \qquad \text{.... (1.8)}$$

the rate law becomes

$$(\dot{A}) = (\dot{B}) = -(\dot{C}) = -(\dot{D}) = -k_f(A)(B) \qquad \text{.... (1.8a)}$$

for the second-order bimolecular reaction

$$2A \rightarrow C + D \quad .... \ (1.9)$$

the rate law is

$$(\dot{A}) = -2(\dot{C}) = -2(\dot{D}) = -2k_f(A)^2 \quad .... \ (1.9a)$$

If B in Eq. 1.8 is replaced by A, Eq. 1.8a does not formally reduce to Eq. 1.9a; it is evidently necessary to reinterpret the meaning of $(\dot{A})$ in Eq. 1.8a according to the law of mass action given in Eq. 1.5.

A classical example of a second-order bimolecular reaction is the reaction between H_2 and I_2 to form HI, or between two HI molecules to form H_2 and I_2[7,8,9]. It is doubtful that this reaction is of the second order and bimolecular at elevated temperatures.

Representative second-order processes which have been postulated[1] as reactions occurring in flames are the following:

$$OH + H_2 \rightarrow H_2O + H$$
$$H + O_2 \rightarrow OH + O$$
$$O + H_2 \rightarrow OH + H$$
$$O_3 + CO \rightarrow CO_2 + 2O$$
$$OH + CH_4 \rightarrow H_2O + CH_3$$

(*C*) *Third-order processes*

An example[10] of a third-order and termolecular reaction is the following:

$$2NO + O_2 \rightarrow 2NO_2$$

Many of the other known termolecular reactions obeying third-order kinetics involve NO (e.g., reaction with H_2, Cl_2, I_2).

1.3. Simultaneous, Interdependent, Chemical Reactions

In general, chemical reactions can proceed in both the forward direction (reactants forming products, rate constant k_f) and in the reverse direction (reaction products reforming the reactants, rate constant k_b). At thermodynamic equilibrium there is no net change in composition. Hence the rate constants k_f and k_b must be related through the equilibrium constant, K_c, expressed in terms of the ratio of concentrations raised to appropriate powers.

The general set of opposing chemical reactions

$$\sum_{j=1}^{n} \nu_j' M_j \underset{k_b}{\overset{k_f}{\rightleftarrows}} \sum_{j=1}^{n} \nu_j'' M_j \quad .... \ (1.10)$$

can also be written in the form

$$\left.\begin{aligned} \sum_{j=1}^{n} \nu_j' M_j &\xrightarrow{k_f} \sum_{j=1}^{n} \nu_j'' M_j \\ \sum_{j=1}^{n} \nu_j'' M_j &\xrightarrow{k_b} \sum_{j=1}^{n} \nu_j' M_j \end{aligned}\right\} \quad .... \ (1.10a)$$

where the appropriate rate-constants are indicated explicitly over the arrows. For simultaneous chemical reactions, the basic rate law of Eq. 1.5 must be applied to each reaction step and $(\dot{M}_i)$ represents the sum of the changes produced by the individual simultaneous reaction steps. Thus, for the reaction symbolized by Eq. 1.10 or Eq. 1.10a,

$$(\dot{M}_i) = (\nu_i'' - \nu_i')k_f \prod_{j=1}^{n} (M_j)^{\nu_j'} + (\nu_i' - \nu_i'')k_b \prod_{j=1}^{n} (M_j)^{\nu_j''} \quad .... \ (1.11)$$

At thermodynamic equilibrium

$$(\dot{M}_i) = 0, \ (M_j) = (M_{j,\,e}) \quad .... \ (1.12)$$

where $(M_{j,\,e})$ denotes the thermodynamic equilibrium value for species M_j. From Eq. 1.11 and 1.12 it follows that

$$k_f/k_b = \prod_{j=1}^{n} (M_{j,\,e})^{\nu_j'' - \nu_j'} \equiv K_c \quad .... \ (1.13)$$

Here K_c represent the usual equilibrium constant defined in terms of concentration ratios. It is evident that Eq. 1.13 relates the ratio of the kinetic parameters k_f and k_b to the thermodynamic equilibrium constant, K_c, which can be calculated quite accurately, for example, by quantum-statistical calculations[11] from molecular properties. Equation 1.11 can be rewritten in terms of K_c as follows:

$$(\dot{M}_i) = (\nu_i'' - \nu_i')k_f \prod_{j=1}^{n} (M_j)^{\nu_j'} [1 - (1/K_c) \prod_{j=1}^{n} (M_j)^{\nu_j'' - \nu_j'}] \quad .... \ (1.14)$$

(*A*) *First-order reaction opposed by a first-order reaction*

Consider the first-order reaction

$$A_1 \underset{k_b}{\overset{k_f}{\rightleftarrows}} B_1$$

for which Eq. 1.11 becomes

$$d(x)/dt = k_f(A_{1,\,o} - x) - k_b(x)$$

if $(A_1) = (A_{1,\,o} - x)$, $(B_1) = (x)$, $(B_{1,\,o}) = 0$, and the subscript o denotes initial concentrations. Also

$$k_f/k_b = K_c = (x_e)/(A_{1,\,o} - x_e) \quad .... \ (1.15)$$

where the subscript e identifies the value of (x) at thermodynamic equilibrium. If $(x) = 0$ at $t = 0$ then it is found that

$$k_f = [(x_e)/(A_{1,\,o})t]\ln[(x_e)/(x_e - x)] \quad .... \ (1.16)$$

Hence if the equilibrium concentration $(x_e) = (B_{1,\,e})$ is known, we can determine both k_f and k_b from experimental measurements of x as a function of time. Equation 1.15 can also be written in the form

$$(x_e)/(A_{1,\,o}) = k_f/(k_f + k_b)$$

whence Eq. 1.16 becomes

$$k_f + k_b = (1/t)\ln[(x_e)/(x_e - x)] \quad \text{.... (1.17)}$$

Equation 1.17 is formally identical with the first-order rate law for the forward reaction alone, viz.,

$$k_f = (1/t)\ln[(A_{1,o})/(A_{1,o} - x)] \quad \text{.... (1.18)}$$

However, it is not difficult to distinguish between the chemical rate processes corresponding to Eq. 1.17 and 1.18, respectively, by studying the reaction rate as a function of the initial concentration $(A_{1,o})$. Equations 1.17 and 1.18 are written in a form suitable for the interpretation of experimental data.

(*B*) *First-order reaction opposed by a second-order reaction*

A first-order reaction opposed by a second-order reaction is represented by the relation

$$A_1 \underset{k_b}{\overset{k_f}{\rightleftarrows}} B_1 + B_2 \quad \text{.... (1.19)}$$

Equation 1.14 becomes

$$d(x)/dt = k_f(A_{1,o} - x) - k_b(x)^2$$

if $(B_{1,o}) = (B_{2,o}) = 0$. The integrated equation is

$$k_f = [x_e/t(2A_{1,o} - x_e)]$$
$$\times \ln\{[(A_{1,o})(x_e) + (x)(A_{1,o} - x_e)]/(A_{1,o})(x_e - x)\} \quad \text{.... (1.20)}$$

(*C*) *Second-order reaction opposed by a second-order reaction*

For the process

$$A_1 + A_2 \underset{k_b}{\overset{k_f}{\rightleftarrows}} B_1 + B_2$$

it is found that

$$k_f = [x_e/2at(a - x_e)]\ln\{[x(a - 2x_e) + ax_e]/a(x_e - x)\} \quad \text{.... (1.21)}$$

if $(A_{1,o}) = (A_{2,o}) = a$ and $(B_{1,o}) = (B_{2,o}) = 0$

(*D*) *Consecutive reactions*

The reaction scheme for two consecutive first-order reaction steps is given by the equation

$$A \xrightarrow{k_f} B \xrightarrow{k_f'} C \quad \text{.... (1.22)}$$

For this process

$$-d(A)/dt = k_f(A)$$

or

$$(A) = (A_o)\exp(-k_f t) \quad \text{.... (1.23)}$$

Similarly,

$$d(C)/dt = k_f'(B) \quad \text{.... (1.24)}$$

and

$$d(B)/dt = k_f(A) - k_f'(B) \quad \text{.... (1.25)}$$

From Eq. 1.23 and 1.25:

$$d(B)/dt = k_f(A_o)\ [\exp(-k_f t)] - k_f'(B)$$

whence

$$(B) = [k_f/(k_f' - k_f)](A_o)[\exp(-k_f t) - \exp(-k_f' t)] \quad \text{.... (1.26)}$$

if $(B_o) = 0$. Also if $(C_o) = 0$ then

$$(A) + (B) + (C) = (A_o) \quad \text{.... (1.27)}$$

By introducing Eq. 1.23 and 1.26 into Eq. 1.27 we obtain an explicit relation for the dependence of (C) on time.

Consecutive reactions of the type listed in Eq. 1.22 play an important role in the decay of radioactive material[12].

The reduction of $KMnO_4$ by $H_2C_2O_4$ to MnO in H_2SO_4 solution can also be understood in terms of the reaction scheme described by Eq. 1.22. During the early phases of reaction, MnO_2 is formed rapidly, slowly oxidized by $KMnO_4$ to Mn_2O_7, and finally reduced by $H_2C_2O_4$ to MnO. Since both $KMnO_4$ and $H_2C_2O_4$ are present in great excess, the observed reaction rate, which depends only on the concentrations of MnO_2 and Mn_2O_7, follows the scheme

$$MnO_2 \xrightarrow{k_f} Mn_2O_7 \xrightarrow{k_f'} MnO$$

The reduction of $KMnO_4$ by $H_2C_2O_4$ in H_2SO_4 solution is an example of a complicated chemical process with relatively simple, slow, and therefore rate-determining, reaction steps.

(*E*) *Various complex reactions*

The reaction between ICl and H_2 obeys the kinetic law[13]

$$-d(ICl)/dt = k_f(ICl)(H_2)$$

which is consistent with the mechanism

$$\begin{aligned} ICl + H_2 &\rightarrow HI + HCl \text{ (slow)} \\ HI + ICl &\rightarrow I_2 + HCl \text{ (very fast)} \end{aligned} \quad \text{.... (1.28)}$$

The reaction is of second order and the rate-controlling step is the slow reaction.

Experimental studies[14] on the reaction between nitric oxide and hydrogen show that the overall order of the reaction varies between 2.60 and 2.89. Variable and fractional overall orders for a reaction indicate a complex reaction mechanism. For the reduction of NO by hydrogen a satisfactory explanation of observed results is obtained by postulating that the reaction occurs according to the following reaction scheme:

$$\left.\begin{aligned} 2NO + H_2 &\rightarrow N_2 + H_2O_2 \quad \text{(slow)} \\ H_2O_2 + H_2 &\rightarrow 2H_2O \qquad\quad \text{(fast)} \end{aligned}\right\} \quad \text{.... (1.29)}$$

A more striking example of a complex reaction mechanism is provided by the formation of HBr from H_2 and Br_2. The overall process is

$$H_2 + Br_2 \rightarrow 2HBr \quad \text{.... (1.30)}$$

The experimental rate law corresponding to the stoichiometric reaction shown in Eq. 1.30 is

$$d(HBr)/dt = C_1(H_2)(Br_2)^{1/2}/\{1 + [(HBr)/C_2(Br_2)]\} \quad \text{.... (1.31)}$$

where C_1 and C_2 are constants at fixed temperature. According to Eq. 1.31 the rate of formation of the reaction product HBr is inhibited by the reaction product. The existence of self-inhibition is unequivocal evidence for an atomic or free radical reaction mechanism. The converse statement is, however, not true since some chain reactions (e.g., the thermal decomposition of some of the lower hydrocarbons) obey simple rate laws. The reaction between H_2 and Br_2 will be discussed in some detail in the following Sec. 1.4.

1.4. Chain Reactions and the Steady-State Treatment for Chain Carriers

We now turn to a discussion of the most common type of chemical reaction, which consists of a series of opposing and successive reaction steps with different reaction rate constants. These complex chemical reactions occur in all technical combustion processes. We shall describe processes which are understood in considerable detail. For technical combustion reactions the specific rate constants for the separate reaction steps are either not known at all or else they have been approximated rather roughly[1].

(*A*) *Steady-state treatment of complex reactions*

A rigorous treatment of complex reactions involves writing the appropriate differential equations for the individual reactions, eliminating the concentrations of intermediate atoms and free radicals, and solving the resulting equations. For all but the very simplest reaction processes a rigorous solution is practically unobtainable. For this reason an approximation, based on the assumption of steady concentrations of reaction intermediates, is customarily introduced. Before describing this steady-state treatment we shall attempt a complete solution for a first-order reaction involving two reaction steps.

According to LINDEMANN's theory[15] for first-order processes, first-order reactions occur as the result of the two-step reaction

$$A + A \underset{k_b}{\overset{k_f}{\rightleftarrows}} A^* + A \qquad \text{(fast)} \qquad .... (1.32)$$

$$A^* \xrightarrow{k_f'} \text{reaction products (slow)} \qquad .... (1.33)$$

Thus, binary collisions are responsible for the formation of energetic molecules A* which then decompose to form the reaction products. The overall process will obey a first-order rate law as long as the formation of A* according to Eq. 1.32 is sufficiently rapid to maintain an equilibrium concentration of A*. Since the frequency of binary collisions decreases as the pressure is reduced, one would expect that the process symbolized by Eq. 1.32 would cease to be fast at reduced pressures and, therefore, first-order reactions should become of the second order at sufficiently low pressures. This change of overall order with pressure is, in fact, observed for many first-order reactions.

The differential equations corresponding to the reaction processes of Eq. 1.32 and 1.33 are

$$d(A^*)/dt = k_f(A)^2 - k_b(A^*)(A) - k'_f(A^*) \qquad .... (1.34)$$

and

$$-d(A)/dt = k_f(A)^2 - k_b(A^*)(A) \qquad .... (1.35)$$

From Eq. 1.35 it is apparent that

$$(A^*) = [k_f(A)^2 + d(A)/dt]/k_b(A) \qquad .... (1.36)$$

and, differentiating,

$$d(A^*)/dt = 2(k_f/k_b)[d(A)/dt] + [k_b(A)]^{-1}[d^2(A)/dt^2] - [k_b(A)^2]^{-1} [d(A)/dt]^2 \qquad .... (1.37)$$

By combining Eq. 1.34, 1.36, and 1.37 we obtain a single second-order differential equation in (A) and t which can be solved exactly only by numerical methods.

We have not yet exploited the result of our postulate that reaction according to Eq. 1.33 is slow compared to the forward and reverse reactions given in Eq. 1.32. This physical notion leads to the conclusion that $d(A^*)/dt$ must be small compared to $d(A)/dt$ and suggests a straightforward iteration procedure for the solution of Eq. 1.34 and 1.35. The first approximation to the solution is the classical steady-state approximation, which is expressed by the relation

$$d(A^*)/dt = 0 \qquad .... (1.38)$$

Equation 1.34 now leads to the expression

$$(A^*) = \frac{k_f(A)^2}{k_b(A) + k_f'} \qquad .... (1.39)$$

which can be combined with Eq. 1.35 to yield the result

$$-\mathrm{d}(\mathrm{A})/\mathrm{d}t = k_f k_f'(\mathrm{A})^2/[k_b(\mathrm{A}) + k_f'] \quad \text{.... (1.40)}$$

This last relation can be integrated directly. Thus, for the chemical process described by Eq. 1.32 and 1.33, introduction of the steady-state approximation of Eq. 1.38 leads to a straightforward solution of the problem.

A steady-state postulate for reaction intermediates is sometimes justified, as a first approximation, for chemical reactions in flow systems. However, it is necessary to examine the conditions in any given problem in order to verify, at least, that the steady-state is possible. The limitations of the steady-state assumption can be assessed most simply by comparing the complete solution with results derived from the steady-state treatment. Unfortunately this programme can be carried through only for the simplest chemical reactions[16]. Hence, considerable ingenuity and physical insight may be required in any given problem in order to obtain a rational estimate for the limits of reliability of the steady-state treatment.

(*B*) *The hydrogen-bromine reaction*

The empirically observed rate law for the overall reaction

$$H_2 + Br_2 \rightarrow 2HBr \quad \text{.... (1.41)}$$

has been given in Eq. 1.31. We shall now derive this relation from our knowledge of the reaction mechanism [17–22] by using the steady-state approximation. In the analysis of complex chemical reactions it is usually convenient to write pairs of opposing reactions as separate reaction steps.

The reaction mechanism for the formation of HBr from the elements H_2 and Br_2 is known to be described by the following set of equations[17–22]

$$X' + Br_2 \xrightarrow{k_1} 2Br + X' \quad \text{.... (1.42)}$$

$$Br + H_2 \xrightarrow{k_2} HBr + H \quad \text{.... (1.43)}$$

$$H + Br_2 \xrightarrow{k_3} HBr + Br \quad \text{.... (1.44)}$$

$$H + HBr \xrightarrow{k_4} H_2 + Br \quad \text{.... (1.45)}$$

$$X' + Br + Br \xrightarrow{k_5} Br_2 + X' \quad \text{.... (1.46)}$$

In Eq. 1.42 and 1.46 the symbol X′ represents a 'third body', i.e. any of the chemical species H, Br, H_2, Br_2, or HBr which may be present. The third body acts as an energy source or sink in chemical reactions. Equation 1.42 is a chain-starting or chain-initiating step; it could occur, without the intervention of a third body, as a photochemical reaction in which the bromine molecule absorbs a light quantum of sufficient energy to dissociate it into atoms; it could also occur when a bromine molecule strikes a surface.

Equations 1.43 and 1.44 represent the chain-carrying reactions in which an atom (either Br or H) is produced for each atom which reacts. Equation 1.45 is the inverse to reaction 1.43; the inverse to reaction 1.44 proceeds relatively slowly and is, therefore, unimportant. Equation 1.46 represents the chain-breaking step; chain breaking according to the process

$$H + H + \text{third body} \rightarrow H_2 + \text{third body}$$

is not of importance in the present case since the concentration of H atoms is generally small compared with that of Br atoms.

The steady-state assumption for (H) and (Br) leads to the following two differential equations:

$$d(H)/dt = 0 = k_2(Br)(H_2) - k_3(H)(Br_2) - k_4(H)(HBr) \quad .... \quad (1.47)$$

$$d(Br)/dt = 0 = 2k_1(Br_2) - k_2(Br)(H_2) + k_3(H)(Br_2) + k_4(H)(HBr) - 2k_5(Br)^2 \quad .... \quad (1.48)$$

Addition of Eq. 1.47 and 1.48 leads to the result

$$(Br) = (k_1/k_5)^{1/2}(Br_2)^{1/2} \quad .... \quad (1.49)$$

which expresses the steady-state bromine atom concentration in terms of an equilibrium constant and of the bromine molecule concentration*.

Introduction of Eq. 1.49 into Eq. 1.47 yields the relation

$$(H) = k_2(H_2)(Br)/[k_3(Br_2) + k_4(HBr)] = k_2(k_1/k_5)^{(1/2)}(H_2)(Br_2)^{(1/2)}/[k_3(Br_2) + k_4(HBr)] \quad .... \quad (1.50)$$

from which the steady-state ratio (H)/(Br) is seen to be

$$(H)/(Br) = k_2(H_2)/[k_3(Br_2) + k_4(HBr)]$$

The available rate constants show that (H)/(Br) is small compared to unity at temperatures below about 2000°K†.

The steady-state relation for

$$d(HBr)/dt = k_2(Br)(H_2) + k_3(H)(Br_2) - k_4(H)(HBr)$$

* For the process

$$X' + 2Br \underset{k_1}{\overset{k_5}{\rightleftharpoons}} Br_2 + X'$$

the equilibrium condition is

$$k_1(Br_2) = k_5(Br)^2$$

or

$$(k_1/k_5)^{(1/2)} = (Br)/(Br_2)^{1/2}$$

i.e., $(k_1/k_5)^{1/2}$ is an equilibrium constant.

† For a recent compilation of rate constants and a discussion of the $H_2 - Br_2$ reactions, see CAMPBELL and HIRSCHFELDER[23].

can now be obtained by replacing (Br) and (H) by their appropriate steady-state values. In this manner it is found that

$$d(HBr)/dt = 2k_2(k_1/k_5)^{(1/2)}(H_2)(Br_2)^{(1/2)}/\{1 + [k_4(HBr)/k_3(Br_2)]\} \quad \ldots. \quad (1.51)$$

The result obtained in Eq. 1.51 agrees with the empirical relation given in Eq. 1.31 if we identify

$$C_1 = 2k_2(k_1/k_5)^{1/2} \text{ and } C_2 = k_3/k_4$$

Additional support for the postulated reaction mechanism and for the validity of Eq. 1.51 can be obtained from a detailed study of individual reaction steps by the use of tracer techniques and spectroscopic methods.

(*C*) *Complex chemical reactions in technical combustion processes*

Comprehensive discussions of reaction mechanisms for technical combustion processes, particularly for hydrocarbon oxidation, are given in the literature*. With the possible exception of the oxidation of relatively simple compounds such as H_2 and CO, the detailed reaction mechanism is understood incompletely. Furthermore, quantitative knowledge regarding the specific reaction-rate constants is notably deficient. For this reason, we shall not reproduce a detailed discussion of specific reaction mechanisms but shall content ourselves with a few general remarks concerning the classification of chain reactions and explosions.

The reaction between H_2 and Br_2 constitutes a chain reaction and we have considered examples of typical reaction steps involved in the propagation of chain reactions, viz., *chain-initiation, chain-carrying, and chain-breaking* steps. To these three types of reaction it is necessary to add another, namely, a *chain-branching* step. A *chain-branching* reaction step leads to the production of more chain-carriers than are consumed. Thus, chain-branching reactions are responsible for the production of progressively larger concentrations of chain-carriers and, unless the chain-branching reactions are balanced by chain-breaking reactions, the reaction rate will increase until it becomes sufficiently rapid to be classified as an explosion. In the reaction between hydrogen and oxygen a chain-initiating step is

$$X' + H_2 \rightarrow 2H + X'$$

a chain-carrying step is

$$OH + H_2 \rightarrow H_2O + H$$

a chain-branching step is

$$H + O_2 \rightarrow OH + O$$

a chain-breaking step is

$$2H + X' \rightarrow H_2 + X'$$

* For example, Chapters I to IV of reference 1.

The type of chain reactions which have been considered thus far may be classified conveniently as *material chains* since the chain-carriers are atoms or free radicals. Chain-propagation may also occur through energetic molecules, in which case we may speak of *energy chains*. An example of a possible energy chain is provided by the following pair of reaction steps:

$$O + O_3 \rightarrow O_2^* + O_2$$
$$O_2^* + O_3 \rightarrow 2O_2 + O$$

where an energetic molecule is identified by an asterisk.

As another example consider the oxidation of carbon monoxide, for which the following reaction steps have been proposed[1,24]:

$$CO + O_2 \rightarrow CO_2 + O \qquad \text{(chain-initiating step)}$$

$$\left.\begin{aligned} X' + O + O_2 &\rightarrow O_3 + X' \\ X' + O + CO &\rightarrow CO_2^* + X' \\ CO_2^* + X' &\rightarrow O + CO + X' \\ CO_2^* + O_2 &\rightarrow CO_2 + O_2^* \end{aligned}\right\} \text{(chain-carrying steps)}$$

$$\left.\begin{aligned} O_3 + CO &\rightarrow CO_2 + 2O \\ CO_2^* + O_2 &\rightarrow CO_2 + 2O \end{aligned}\right\} \text{(chain-branching steps)}$$

$$\left.\begin{aligned} O_3 + CO + M &\rightarrow CO_2 + O_2 + M \\ CO_2^* &\rightarrow CO_2 + h\nu \\ O_2^* &\rightarrow O_2 + h\nu' \end{aligned}\right\} \text{(chain-breaking steps)}$$

In the preceding stoichiometric relations there are examples of interconversion from material chain-carriers (O, O_3) to excited molecules (O_2^*, CO_2^*) which may lead to chain-carrying, chain-branching, or to chain-breaking (by emission of photons of frequency ν or ν').* The observational evidence 'explained' by the postulated reaction mechanism for the oxidation of CO is drawn from spectroscopic studies of flames and from measurements of lower and upper explosion limits[24]. The specific reaction-rate constants for the individual reaction steps are generally not known. There is also no proof that the proposed scheme is either unique or complete in the sense that it will predict the results of future studies under different conditions concerning the oxidation of carbon monoxide. Perhaps the best that can be said is that the detailed reaction steps are consistent with the available observational data. In view of the lack of quantitative rate data, it is evidently not possible to carry through a detailed discussion, for example, of laminar flame propagation in carbon-oxygen mixtures. Finally, it should be noted that the behavior of the C-O_2 system is changed radically by the admixture of small amounts of H_2 or

* The symbols $h\nu$ and $h\nu'$ represent the respective energies associated with photons of frequency ν or ν' if h is Planck's constant.

H_2O[1,25,26], and that the rate-controlling reaction mechanism now involves H, OH, H_2, HO_2, and H_2O as well as O, O_2, CO, CO_2, and O_3.

The deactivation of O_2^* and of CO_2^* as the result of emission of radiation are examples of photochemical reactions. In general, a *photochemical reaction* may be defined as a chemical reaction whose rate depends observably on radiation or which emits non-thermal (i.e., non-equilibrium) radiation. Chemical reactions are of two types: either *homogeneous* reactions or *heterogeneous* reactions. The former occur in a homogeneous phase, for example, in an all gaseous system; heterogeneous reactions, on the other hand, are characterized by their preferential occurrence at an interface such as the surface of a solid or liquid. As a rough qualitative guide it is desirable to note that surface reactions are more important at low than at elevated temperatures and are, in any case, not understood well enough to permit the quantitative consideration of surface effects in flow systems involving combustion.

Explosions are conveniently classified into two distinct categories: *branched-chain explosions*, in which the reaction rate increases without limit because of chain-branching, and *thermal explosions*, in which the reaction rate becomes very large because of an exponential increase in reaction rate as the result of exothermic chemical reactions, heating of reactants, and an increase in the magnitude of the specific reaction rate constants.

1.5. Rate Laws for Isothermal Reactions Utilizing Dimensionless Parameters

For the sake of brevity we shall restrict the following discussion to a pair of opposing chemical reactions. Generalization to chain reactions can be introduced without difficulty.

For the most general opposing chemical reaction

$$\sum_{j=1}^{n} \nu_j' M_j \rightleftarrows \sum_{j=1}^{n} \nu_j'' M_j \qquad \text{.... (1.52)}$$

it has been shown in Sec. 1.3 that the net rate of production of species M_i is given by the phenomenological relation

$$(\dot{M}_i) = (\nu_i'' - \nu_i')k_f \prod_{j=1}^{n} (M_j)^{\nu_j'} [1 - (1/K_c) \prod_{j=1}^{n} (M_j)^{\nu_j'' - \nu_j'}] \qquad \text{.... (1.53)}$$

where

$$K_c = k_f/k_b = \prod_{j=1}^{n} (M_{j,\,e})^{\nu_j'' - \nu_j'} \qquad \text{.... (1.54)}$$

We shall now determine relations equivalent to Eq. 1.53 and 1.54 by replacing concentrations by partial pressures, mole fractions, weight fractions, etc. The transformations will be accomplished by assuming the validity of the ideal gas law, which constitutes an adequate approximation for a large class of problems in combustion.

(*A*) *Equilibrium constants*

For ideal gases

$$(M_{j,e}) = p_{j,e}/RT \qquad \text{.... (1.55)}$$

where $p_{j,e}$ denotes the equilibrium partial pressure of the chemical species identified by the symbol M_j and R is the molar gas constant.* If the equilibrium constant K_p is defined by the relation

$$K_p = \prod_{j=1}^{n} (p_{j,e})^{\nu_j'' - \nu_j'} \qquad \text{.... (1.56)}$$

then it is apparent from Eq. 1.54, 1.55, and 1.56 that

$$k_f/k_b = K_c = K_p(RT)^{-\Delta n},\ \Delta n = \sum_{j=1}^{n} (\nu_j'' - \nu_j') \qquad \text{.... (1.57)}$$

For ideal gases the equilibrium mole fraction of species j, $X_{j,e}$, is given by the expression

$$X_{j,e} = p_{j,e}/p_T = (M_{j,e})/(M_T) \qquad \text{.... (1.58)}$$

where p_T represents the total pressure and (M_T) is the total number of moles per unit volume of gas mixture. From Eq. 1.54 to 1.57 we obtain the relation

$$k_f/k_b = K_c = K_p(RT)^{-\Delta n} = K_X(p_T/RT)^{\Delta n} = K_X(M_T)^{\Delta n} \qquad \text{.... (1.59)}$$

where

$$K_X = \prod_{j=1}^{n} (X_{j,e})^{\nu_j'' - \nu_j'} \qquad \text{.... (1.60)}$$

For an ideal gas the equilibrium mass of species j per unit volume, $\rho_{j,e}$, is

$$\rho_{j,e} = (p_{j,e}/RT)W_j = (M_{j,e})W_j \qquad \text{.... (1.61)}$$

where W_j represents the molecular weight of species j. The equilibrium weight fraction of species j is then

$$Y_{j,e} = \rho_{j,e}/\rho_e \qquad \text{.... (1.62)}$$

where $\rho = \rho_e$ denotes the equilibrium density of the fluid mixture. Using the preceding relations it is readily shown that

$$k_f/k_b = K_c = K_p(RT)^{-\Delta n} = K_X(p_T/RT)^{\Delta n} = K_Y F_W^{-1} \rho_e^{\Delta n} = K_\rho F_W^{-1} \qquad \text{.... (1.63)}$$

* An appropriate set of units would specify concentrations in moles/cm³ and partial pressures in atmos, in which case $R = 82.05$ cm³-atmos-mole⁻¹-(degree K)⁻¹.

where

$$K_\rho = \prod_{j=1}^{n} (\rho_{j,e})^{\nu_j'' - \nu_j'} \qquad \text{.... (1.64)}$$

$$F_W = \prod_{j=1}^{n} (W_j)^{\nu_j'' - \nu_j'} \qquad \text{.... (1.65)}$$

and

$$K_Y = \prod_{j=1}^{n} (Y_{j,e})^{\nu_j'' - \nu_j'} \qquad \text{.... (1.66)}$$

It is clear by referring to the definitions of the various quantities involved that only for $\Delta n = 0$ are k_f/k_b, K_c, K_p and F_W dimensionless quantities. However, the equilibrium constants defined in terms of mole fractions (K_X) or in terms of weight fractions (K_Y) are always dimensionless. For use in Eq. 1.53 all of the expressions given in Eq. 1.63 to 1.66 are equivalent since the group

$$(k_b/k_f) \prod_{j=1}^{n} (M_j)^{\nu_j'' - \nu_j'}$$

is always dimensionless. If we define quantities K_c', P_p', K_X', K_ρ', and K_Y' analogous to the equilibrium constants except that concentrations, partial pressures, etc., refer to the prevailing local concentrations, partial pressures, etc., rather than to equilibrium for the local conditions at T and p_T, then it is clear that

$$(k_b/k_f) \prod_{j=1}^{n} (M_j)^{\nu_j'' - \nu_j'} = K_c'/K_c = K_p'/K_p = K_X'/K_X$$
$$= K_\rho'/K_\rho = K_Y'/K_Y \equiv K'/K$$

(*B*) *Net rate of production of chemical species*

By utilizing the definitions introduced in the preceding paragraph the following equivalent expressions are obtained readily for $(\dot{M}_i)$:

$$(\dot{M}_i) = (\nu_i'' - \nu_i') k_f [1 - (K'/K)] \prod_{j=1}^{n} (M_j)^{\nu_j'}$$
$$= (\nu_i'' - \nu_i') k_f (RT)^{-m} [1 - (K'/K)] \prod_{j=1}^{n} (p_j)^{\nu_j'}, m = \sum_{j=1}^{n} \nu_j'$$
$$= (\nu_i'' - \nu_i') k_f (M_T)^m [1 - (K'/K)] \prod_{j=1}^{n} (X_j)^{\nu_j'}$$
$$= (\nu_i'' - \nu_i') k_f [1 - (K'/K)] \prod_{j=1}^{n} (\rho_j/W_j)^{\nu_j'}$$
$$= (\nu_i'' - \nu_i') k_f [1 - (K'/K)] \rho^m \prod_{j=1}^{n} (Y_j/W_j)^{\nu_j'} \qquad \text{.... (1.67)}$$

In Eq. 1.67 the quantities p_j, X_j, ρ_j, and Y_j denote, respectively, partial pressure, mole fraction, mass per unit volume, and weight fraction of species j if the concentration of species j is (M_j).

1.6. The Specific Reaction-Rate Constant; Theoretical Chemical Kinetics*

Throughout the preceding discussion we have treated the specific reaction rate constant, k_i, as a parameter which must be determined empirically. The dependence of k_i on temperature has been established through a great variety of experimental measurements and has been confirmed also by theoretical studies which are summarized briefly in Sec. 1.6*B* and 1.6*C*.

(*A*) *Formal description of the rate law*

The specific reaction rate constant for first-, second-, and third-order chemical reactions is given by a relation of the form

$$k_i = BT^{\alpha}[\exp(-E/RT)] \qquad \text{.... (1.68)}$$

where B is called the frequency factor, E represents the activation energy per mole for the reaction, T equals the absolute temperature, and R is the molar gas constant. The parameter α is generally close to unity and can usually be set equal to zero by modifying slightly the temperature-independent parameters B and E. If $\alpha=0$, Eq. 1.68 reduces to the classical Arrhenius equation for the specific reaction rate. The theoretical calculation of B, α, and especially of E constitutes the subject matter of theoretical chemical kinetics and may be attempted either in terms of the *collision theory* (Sec. 1.6*B*) or else in terms of the *theory of absolute reaction rates* (Sec. 1.6*C*). For many practical applications it is sufficient to utilize the functional form which is given for k_i in Eq. 1.68. Because of the exponential term in Eq. 1.68, and especially for large values of E, k_i will, in general, increase very rapidly as the temperature is increased. The activation energy E is greater than or equal to the heat of reaction for the reaction proceeding in the indicated direction.† For example, the reaction

$$OH + H_2 \rightarrow H_2O + H$$

requires at least the absorption of 9 kcals/mole. Hence $E \geqslant 9$ kcals/mole. Sometimes it is convenient to multiply Eq. 1.68 by another factor Z', which is equal to, or less than, unity. The factor Z' is then referred to as a *steric factor* and is supposed to account for the fact that

* The reader who is primarily interested in the phenomenological description of chemical reactions in flow systems may omit this section, detailed knowledge of which is not needed for the material discussed in subsequent chapters.

† It should be noted that E is always positive or zero, even for exothermic chemical reactions for which the heat of reaction is negative (i.e., heat is evolved).

collisions which would normally lead to reaction do not lead to reaction because of unfavorable orientation of the molecules on collision.

(*B*) *Collision theory of chemical reaction rates*

The collision theory of chemical reaction rates and application of statistical mechanics to the study of reaction rates is described in several excellent treatises[27-29]. The following statements are a summary of the material presented by FOWLER and GUGGENHEIM[29].

It is known from statistical considerations that the number of binary collisions is roughly proportional to $T^{1/2}$. However, the numerical values of E in Eq. 1.68 are such that for many chemical reactions the reaction rate is doubled for a temperature rise of about 10° K near room temperature. Hence, it follows that the particular collisions leading to chemical reactions must be selected from all of the collisions by a special process. It is found that only those relatively few collisions in which the total available energy exceeds a fixed minimum energy can lead to chemical reactions. The questions which must be answered by a theory of reaction rates are: (a) What are the particular energetic conditions required for chemical reaction; (b) How can one calculate, by the use of statistical methods, the frequency of occurrence of effective collisions? The use of statistical methods implies a special type of equilibrium assumption, namely, the equilibrium

$$\text{average molecules} \rightleftarrows \text{energetic molecules}$$

must be established very rapidly compared to the rate at which energetic molecules are consumed by chemical reactions. Although this equilibrium assumption appears to be closely approximated for slow reactions in isothermal systems, it may break down in combustion flames or in explosions where the chemical reaction rates become very large. Thus, there are theoretical grounds on which the applicability of reaction rates determined under isothermal conditions to regions of active combustion may be questioned.

The results of straightforward but lengthy statistical calculations[25–29] applied to collisions between rigid elastic spheres without intermolecular attractions are summarized by the following statements: (a) N.V.T.† with total relative translational energy of the colliding molecules $\geqslant \epsilon^*$

$$= \mathcal{Z}[\exp(-\epsilon^*/kT)][(\epsilon^*/kT)+1] \qquad \text{.... (1.69)}$$

where $\mathcal{Z}$ is the total number of bimolecular collisions per unit time per unit volume and k represents the Boltzmann constant.
(b) N.V.T. with relative translational energy along the line of centers of the colliding molecules $\geqslant \epsilon^*$

$$= \mathcal{Z}\exp(-\epsilon^*/kt) \qquad \text{.... (1.70)}$$

† N.V.T. = number of collisions per unit volume per unit time.

(c) N.V.T. with the sum of the total relative translational energy and of the energy of s vibrators $\geqslant \epsilon^*$

$$=Z[\exp(-\epsilon^*/kt)]\sum_{r=0}^{s+1}(1/r!)(\epsilon^*/kT)^r \quad .... \ (1.71)$$

(d) N.V.T. with the sum of the relative translational energy along the line of centers and the energy of s vibrators $\geqslant \epsilon^*$

$$=Z[\exp(-\epsilon^*/kT)]\sum_{r=0}^{s}(1/r!)(\epsilon^*/kT)^r \quad .... \ (1.72)$$

As a rough approximation, in counting the number of vibrations we include only those frequencies, in determining the value of s, for which $h\nu < kT$ where h is Planck's constant and ν is the vibration frequency in question. The possibility of having rotational energy contribute to ϵ^* can be included also by noting that each translational degree of freedom (of which there are three in each molecule) can contribute energy kT, each vibrational degree of freedom can contribute energy $2\,kT$, and each rotational degree of freedom (of which there are two for linear molecules and three for non-linear molecules) can contribute the energy kT to ϵ^*. If t is the total number of energy contributions of magnitude kT then it can be shown that N.V.T. (for t energy contributions of magnitude kT) $\geqslant \epsilon^*$

$$=Z[\exp(-\epsilon^*/kT)]\sum_{r=0}^{t/2}[1/\Gamma(t+1)](\epsilon^*/kT)^r \quad .... \ (1.73)$$

if t is even; for odd values of t the lower limit of the sum in Eq. 1.73 becomes $r=1/2$ and a (usually very small) term of order $(\epsilon^*/kT)^{-1/2}$ must be added to the summation. Here $\Gamma(t)$ denotes the gamma function of t. For many chemical reactions ϵ^*/kT is so large that it is sufficient to retain only the first term in the expressions for N.V.T.

Equations 1.69 to 1.73 contain the most elaborate results of the collision theory of chemical reaction rates by which experimental data are explained. The results are consistent in one important respect: the quantity N.V.T. for total energy greater than, or equal to, the critical energy ϵ^* always varies as $Z[\exp(-\epsilon^*/kT)]$ and may contain additional factors which, however, depend relatively weakly on temperature.

Experimental measurements of the specific reaction rate k_f for the process

$$2HI \rightarrow H_2 + I_2, \ 550 \leqslant T, \ °K \leqslant 789$$

show that the experimental data are correlated equally well by the relations (k_f in cm^3 per molecule per sec):

$$k_f = 8 \times 10^{-11} \exp(-22{,}000/T)$$
$$k_f = 2 \times 10^{-9} T^{-(1/2)} \exp(-22{,}000/T)$$
$$k_f = 3 \times 10^{-12} T^{(1/2)} \exp(-22{,}000/T)$$

Detailed comparison with Eq. 1.69 and 1.73 shows that the experimental rate data are predicted quite accurately if the *critical collisions leading to chemical reactions are determined by the relative translational energy along the line of centers.* The semi-quantitative successes of the collision theory of reaction rates are largely restricted to the reaction between two HI molecules or between H_2 and I_2 molecules.

Although the collision theory cannot be used to predict absolute values for reaction-rate constants, it is a valuable tool for the study of collision processes between complex molecules. The observed reaction rates yield information about energy transfer on collision.

(*C*) *The theory of absolute reaction rates*

Most of the recent attempts at calculating reaction velocities have been made by use of the theory of absolute reaction rates developed particularly by EYRING, POLANYI, and WIGNER[30]. Semi-empirical methods have been developed for calculating activation energies from first principles, following basic work of HEITLER and LONDON[31], SLATER[32], and others. In spite of the unquestioned successes of this method of approach, it can hardly be said that a reliable calculation, either of activation energy or of specific reaction rate, can be carried out for any but the very simplest chemical reactions and, even for these, approximations must be made. For this reason, it is perhaps justifiable to conclude that the theoretical analysis has not yet advanced to the point where a significant contribution can be made to the solution of technical combustion reactions. A detailed discussion of the modern theory of rate processes is given by GLASSTONE *et al*[30] and requires knowledge of wave mechanics. For the present purposes it will be sufficient to present an elementary account of the method of approach. The following treatment is not intended to be either rigorous or exhaustive.

In the same manner as the collision theory of chemical reactions, the theory of absolute reaction rates starts with molecular collisions. Under favorable conditions, the collisions lead to the formation of a transitory chemical species, the *activated complex*. By use of the methods of quantum mechanics, it is possible, in principle, to calculate the forces between atoms and molecules. A detailed description of the activated complex will provide insight into the nature of the changes in electronic and nuclear arrangement which characterize the chemical reaction. Consider the reaction between reactants A and B to form the reaction products C and D. The formation of reaction products is preceded by the production of an aggregate designated by the symbol $X_{\ddagger}$ which is called the *activated complex*. Thus

$$A+B \rightleftarrows X_{\ddagger} \rightleftarrows C+D \qquad .... \; (1.74)$$

We may associate with the path from reactants to reaction products a coordinate, the 'reaction coordinate'. Depending on the choice of the reaction coordinate, there will be different amounts of energy required for the reaction described by Eq. 1.74. The activated complex is located at the point of highest energy on the most favorable reaction path and the activation energy ϵ^* per molecule is required to form $X_\ddagger$ (see *Fig. 1.2*). For the most favorable reaction path the highest point ($X_\ddagger$) has lower potential energy above the reactants (namely, $E = \mathcal{N}\epsilon^*$ per mole) than for any other reaction path.

In the equilibrium theory of reaction rates the assumption is made that the equilibrium between $X_\ddagger$ and reactants is maintained, for all practical purposes, even though $X_\ddagger$ is decomposing*. In order to calculate the reaction rate we utilize the equilibrium between $X_\ddagger$ and reactants to estimate the concentration ($X_\ddagger$) of activated molecules and multiply this result by the frequency of crossing of the energy barrier.

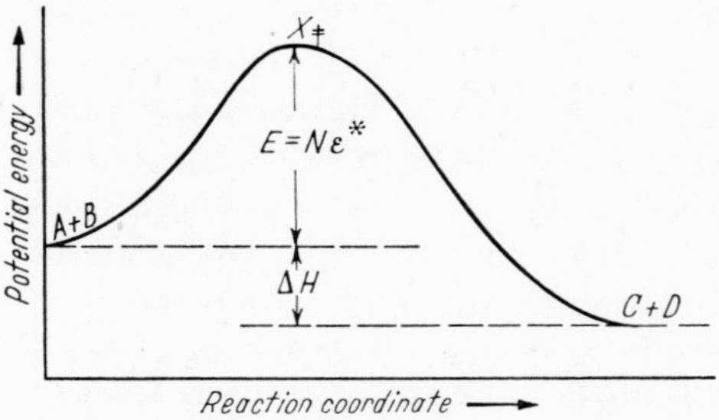

Fig. 1.2. Variation of potential energy along the reaction coordinate (E = activation energy per mole, ΔH = heat of reaction, $\mathcal{N}$ = Avogadro number).

Using the equilibrium assumption and statistical thermodynamics it is easily shown that

$$(X_\ddagger)/(A)(B) = [(Q_{tr}Q_{rot}Q_{vibr}Q_{el})_{X_\ddagger}/(Q_{tr}Q_{rot}Q_{vibr}Q_{el})_A(Q_{tr}Q_{rot}Q_{vibr}Q_{el})_B] \times [\exp(-\epsilon^*/kT)] \quad .... \quad (1.75)$$

where Q_{tr} = translational partition function per unit volume, Q_{rot} = rotational partition function, Q_{vibr} = vibrational partition function, Q_{el} = electronic partition function†, and the activation energy ϵ^* has been identified with the minimum difference in energy between the activated state and the reactants. In first approximation, the normal vibrational frequencies can be calculated by applying the 'theory of small vibrations' to the activated complex. Detailed calculations show that one of the frequencies of the activated state always has an

* Calculations[33,34] have been carried out without this equilibrium assumption. The order of magnitude of the results is generally not changed.

† The partition function is defined as $\sum_{i=1}^{\infty} g_i[\exp(-\epsilon_i/kT)]$ where ϵ_i is the energy of the i'th (rotational, vibrational, or electronic) energy level above the ground level and g_i is the statistical weight of the i'th level, i.e. the number of states with energy ϵ.

According to the quantum theory the energy associated with a harmonic oscillator of frequency ν_i is $h\nu_i[n + (1/2)]$. Hence the minimum energy or *zero-point* energy is $(1/2)h\nu_i$.

imaginary value $i\nu_{\ddagger}$ where $i=\sqrt{-1}$. For the motion of the atoms which is associated with the frequency $\nu_{\ddagger}$ the activated state is unstable and decomposes. It can be shown that the contribution of the vibration of frequency $\nu_{\ddagger}$ to $(Q_{vibr})_{X\ddagger}$ leads to a factor of the form $kT/h\nu_{\ddagger}$. Hence we may write

$$(Q_{vibr})_{X\ddagger} = (kT/h\nu_{\ddagger})(Q'_{vibr})_{X\ddagger}$$

and Eq. 1.75 becomes

$$\nu_{\ddagger}(X_{\ddagger}) = (A)(B)(kT/h)(Q_{tr}Q_{rot}Q'_{vibr}Q_{el})_{X\ddagger}(Q_{tr}Q_{rot}Q_{vibr}Q_{el})_A^{-1} \times (Q_{tr}Q_{rot}Q_{vibr}Q_{el})_B^{-1}[\exp(-\epsilon^*/kT)] \quad .... \ (1.76)$$

But $\nu_{\ddagger}(X_{\ddagger})$ is the frequency of decomposition of activated complexes and therefore represents the overall reaction rate. The specific reaction rate, k_f, is simply $\nu_{\ddagger}(X_{\ddagger})/(A)(B)$, i.e.,

$$k_f = (kT/h)(Q_{tr}Q_{rot}Q'_{vibr}Q_{el})_{X\ddagger}(Q_{tr}Q_{rot}Q_{vibr}Q_{el})_A^{-1} \times (Q_{tr}Q_{rot}Q_{vibr}Q_{el})_B^{-1}[\exp(-\epsilon^*/kT)] \quad .... \ (1.77)$$

The quantity kT/h has the numerical value 6×10^{12} sec^{-1} at 300° K. In practice it is necessary to multiply the right-hand side of Eq. 1.77 by a transmission factor κ which measures the probability that $X_{\ddagger}$ will decompose to C and D rather than to A and B. The ratio of partition functions may be regarded as a modified equilibrium constant.

Explicit calculations of k_f according to Eq. 1.77 requires detailed knowledge of the structures of A, B, and $X_{\ddagger}$. The partition functions are then evaluated by the use of well-known procedures, viz.,

$$Q_{tr} = (2\pi mkT)^{3/2}/h^3 \quad .... \ (1.78)$$

$$Q_{rot}f(\text{sym}) = \begin{cases} 1 \text{ for atoms;} \\ 8\pi^2 IkT/h^2 \text{ for linear molecules with moment of inertia } I; \\ (8\pi^2 IkT)^{3/2}/h^3 \text{ for spherical top molecules, i.e., for molecules with three equal moments of inertia } I; \\ (8\pi^2 kT)^{3/2} I(I')^{1/2}/h^3 \text{ for symmetric-top molecules, i.e., for molecules with two equal moments of inertia } I \text{ and the third moment of inertia equal to } I'; \\ (8\pi^2 kT)^{3/2}(I I' I'')^{1/2}/h^3 \text{ for asymmetric-top molecules, i.e., for molecules with three unequal moments of inertia } I, I', I''; \end{cases} \quad .... \ (1.79)$$

$$Q_{vibr} = \begin{cases} 1 \text{ for atoms;} \\ \prod_{i=1}^{\xi}[1-\exp(-h\nu_i/kT)]^{-1} \text{ where } \xi = 3n-5 \text{ for linear molecules and } \xi = 3n-6 \text{ for non-linear molecules with n representing the total number of atoms in the molecule;} \end{cases} \quad .... \ (1.80)$$

$$Q_{el} = \sum_i g_{el,\,i}[\exp(-\epsilon_{el,\,i}/kT)] \simeq g_o, \quad .... \ (1.81)$$

i.e., the statistical weight for the ground electronic level for most atoms and molecules at ordinary temperatures. Here m is the mass of the molecule; I, I', and I'' denote appropriate moments of inertia of the molecules; ν_i represents the i'th normal vibration frequency of the molecule. The quantity f(sym) depends on the symmetry properties of the nucleus and of the electronic and rotational wave functions. For the sake of simplicity we shall make the assumption that $f(\text{sym}) = 1$ in our illustrative examples although this assumption is not generally valid. It is apparent that quantitative calculations of the pre-exponential factor in Eq. 1.77 can be carried out only if the structure of $X_\ddagger$ can be specified in sufficient detail to permit calculation of partition functions for the activated state. In this connection it should be noted that the upper limit in the product for $(Q'_{\text{vibr}})_{X\ddagger}$ has the value $3n-6$ for linear molecules and $3n-7$ for non-linear molecules since one of the vibrational frequencies of the activated state, namely, the low vibration frequency leading to decomposition of $X_\ddagger$ and to formation of the reaction products, has already been used in the derivation of Eq. 1.77. Finally, absolute values of k_f can be determined only if ϵ^* is known or can be calculated. As was mentioned earlier in this discussion, some measure of success has been achieved in the theoretical calculations of ϵ^* by using semi-empirical rules developed particularly by Eyring. For the present purposes it will be sufficient to illustrate the use of Eq. 1.77 in calculating k_f for several simple cases.

(*1*) *Reaction between atom* A *and atom* B—The stoichiometric relation for the reaction becomes

$$A + B \rightleftarrows X_\ddagger \rightarrow \text{reaction products} \qquad \text{.... (1.82)}$$

The diatomic molecule $X_\ddagger$ is necessarily linear and has but one normal vibration frequency ($3 \times$ number of atoms $-5 = 3 \times 2 - 5 = 1$). This frequency has already been used in the derivation of Eq. 1.77 whence $(Q_{\text{vibr}}')_{X\ddagger} = 1$. Also $(Q_{\text{tr}})_{X\ddagger} = [2\pi(m_A + m_B)kT]^{3/2}/h^3$, $(Q_{\text{rot}})_{X\ddagger} = 8\pi^2 I_{X\ddagger} kT/h^2$, $(Q_{\text{tr}})_A = (2\pi m_A kT)^{3/2}/h^3$, $(Q_{\text{tr}})_B = (2\pi m_B kT)^{3/2}/h^3$, $I_{X\ddagger} = [m_A m_B/(m_A + m_B)] r_{AB\ddagger}^2$ if $r_{AB\ddagger}$ is the distance between A and B in the activated state $X_\ddagger$. Introducing these expressions in Eq. 1.77 and using a transmission coefficient $\kappa (0 \leqslant \kappa \leqslant 1)$ it is found that

$$k_f = \kappa r_{AB\ddagger}^2 [8\pi kT(m_A + m_B)/m_A m_B]^{1/2} [\exp(-\epsilon^*/kT)]$$
$$= \kappa Z \exp(-\epsilon^*/kT) \qquad \text{.... (1.83)}$$

where Z represents, as in Sec. 1.6*B*, the total number of bimolecular collisions per unit time per unit volume if $r_{AB\ddagger}$ is identified with the kinetic theory collision diameter. It is interesting to note that for chemical reactions between two atoms the theory of absolute reaction rates gives a result which is identical with the relation obtained from the collision theory (cf. Eq. 1.70) except for the transmission factor κ, provided the energy of activation for reaction between atoms in the collision theory is made up of the relative translational energy along the line of centers. It will be recalled that this last assumption was also found to be in good accord with the empirical rate measurements on reaction between two HI molecules at moderate temperatures.

(2) *Reaction between atom* A *and diatomic molecule* B—The stoichiometric equation becomes

$$A + B \rightleftarrows X_\ddagger \text{ (a linear triatomic molecule) } \rightarrow \text{reaction products.}$$

.... (1.84)

Using Eq. 1.78 to 1.80 with $Q_{el} = 1$, it is readily shown that

$$k_f = \kappa (m_{X\ddagger}/m_A m_B)^{3/2} (I_{X\ddagger}/I_B) [h^2/(8\pi^3 kT)^{1/2}][1 - \exp(-h\nu_B/kT)]$$

$$\times \prod_{i=1}^{3} [1 - \exp(-h\nu_{\ddagger, i}/kT)]^{-1}[\exp(-\epsilon^*/kT)] \quad \text{.... (1.85)}$$

where we have omitted the factors determined by f(sym). In Eq. 1.85 $m_{X\ddagger} = m_A + m_B$; ν_B = the vibrational frequency of the diatomic molecule B; $\nu_{\ddagger, i}$ = the 3 unused vibrational frequencies of $X_\ddagger$, which are known only if the structure of $X_\ddagger$ (which is always a linear molecule) can be specified precisely.

(3) *Reaction between diatomic molecule* $A_1 A_2$ *and diatomic molecule* $B_1 B_2$—For reaction between two diatomic molecules the activated state has a non-linear structure of the form

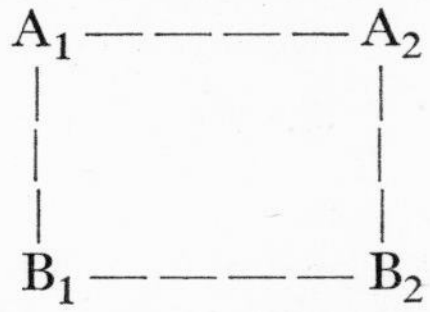

$$
\begin{array}{ccc}
A_1 & ----- & A_2 \\
| & & | \\
| & & | \quad (X_\ddagger) \\
| & & | \\
B_1 & ----- & B_2
\end{array}
$$

with $12 - 7 = 5$ unknown normal vibration frequencies. In several cases it has proved to be possible to approximate $X_\ddagger$ sufficiently closely to permit explicit calculations[30] of partition functions.

(4) *Unimolecular decomposition of complex molecules*—For the unimolecular decomposition of the asymmetric-top molecule X according to the process

$$X \rightleftarrows X_\ddagger \rightarrow \text{reaction products}$$

it is readily shown that

$$k_f = \kappa (I_{X\ddagger} I_{X\ddagger}' I_{X\ddagger}''/I_X I_X' I_X'')^{1/2} \prod_{i=1}^{3n-7} [1 - \exp(-h\nu_{\ddagger, i}/kT)]^{-1}$$

$$\times \prod_{j=1}^{3n-6} [1 - \exp(-h\nu_j/kT)](kT/h)[\exp(-\epsilon^*/kT)] \quad \text{.... (1.86)}$$

where the I_X and $I_{X\ddagger}$ denote appropriate moments of inertia and the ν_j are the known vibration frequencies of the reactant.

Explicit calculations of k_f for unimolecular decomposition reactions can usually not be carried out because, as for most other chemical reactions, the detailed structure of $X_\ddagger$ is not known.

REFERENCES

1 Lewis, B., and von Elbe, G., *Combustion, Flames, and Explosions of Gases*, Academic Press, Inc., New York, 1951

2 Blanksma, J. J., *Rec. Trav. chim. Pays-Bas* 21 (1902) 366; 22 (1903) 290

3 Daniels, F., and Johnston, E. H., *J. Amer. chem. Soc.* 43 (1921) 53

4 Eyring, H., and Daniels, F., *J. Amer. chem. Soc.* 52 (1930) 1472

5 Sickman, D. V., and Rice, O. K., *J. chem. Phys.* 4 (1936) 608

6 Hinshelwood, C. N., *et al.*, *Proc. roy. Soc.* A200 (1950) 458; A201 (1950) 18; A203 (1950) 486; A208 (1951) 285; A214 (1952) 20

7 Bodenstein, M., *Z. phys. Chem.* 13 (1894) 56; 22 (1897) 1; 29 (1899) 295

8 Taylor, H. A., *J. phys. Chem.* 28 (1924) 984

9 Kistiakowsky, G. B., *J. Amer. chem. Soc.* 50 (1928) 2315

10 Bodenstein, M., *Z. phys. Chem.* 100 (1922) 68

11 Mayer, J. E., and Mayer, M. G., *Statistical Mechanics*, John Wiley and Sons, New York, 1940

12 Rutherford, E., and Soddy, F., *J. chem. Soc.* 81 (1902) 321, 837

13 Bonner, W. D., Gore, W. L., and Yost, D. M., *J. Amer. chem. Soc.* 57 (1935) 2723

14 Hinshelwood, C. N., and Green, T. E., *J. chem. Soc.* 129 (1926) 730

15 Lindemann, F. A., *Trans. Faraday Soc.* 17 (1922) 598

16 Benson, S. W., *J. chem. Phys.* 20 (1952) 1605

17 Bodenstein, M., *Z. phys. Chem.* 85 (1913) 329

18 Nernst, W., *Z. Elektrochem.* 24 (1918) 335

19 Christiansen, J. A., *Mat.-fys. Medd. danske vidensk. Selsk.* 1 (1919) 14

20 Herzfeld, K. F., *Z. Elektrochem.* 25 (1919) 301

21 — *Ann. Phys., Lpz.* 59 (1919) 635

22 Polanyi, M., *Z. Elektrochem.* 26 (1920) 50

23 Campbell, E. S., and Hirschfelder, J. O., "Review of the Reaction Kinetics and Transport Properties of a Hydrogen-Bromine Flame", University of Wisconsin Naval Research Laboratory, Report CF-2108, November 17, 1953

24 Griffing, V. F., and Laidler, K. J., *Third Symposium on Combustion and Flame and Explosion Phenomena*, p. 432, The Williams and Wilkins Co., Baltimore, 1949. Laidler, K. J., *t. c.* p. 441

25 Lewis, B., *J. Amer. chem. Soc.* 55 (1933) 4001

26 Groth, W., and Harteck, P., *Z. Elektrochem.* 44 (1938) 621

27 Kassel, L. S., *The Kinetics of Homogeneous Gas Reactions*, The Chemical Catalog Co., Inc., New York, 1932

28 Hinshelwood, C. N., *The Kinetics of Chemical Change*, Clarendon Press, Oxford, 1947

29 Fowler, R. H., and Guggenheim, E. A., *Statistical Thermodynamics*, Cambridge Univ. Pr., New York, 1939

30 Glasstone, S., Laidler, K. J., and Eyring, H., *The Theory of Rate Processes*, McGraw-Hill Book Co., Inc., New York, 1941

31 Heitler, W., and London, F., *Z. Phys.* 44 (1927) 455

32 Slater, J. C., *Phys. Rev.* 38 (1931) 1109

33 Kramers, H. A., *Physica* 7 (1940) 284

34 Zwolinski, B. J., and Eyring, H., *J. Amer. chem. Soc.* 69 (1947) 270

CHAPTER 2

CONSERVATION LAWS AND TRANSPORT COEFFICIENTS IN REACTING MIXTURES

THE solution of flow problems with chemical reactions requires not only knowledge of the rates of chemical changes, but also of appropriate forms of the conservation equations in reacting gas mixtures. Utilization of these, in turn, depends upon the availability of explicit relations for the transport coefficients. For this reason it may be in order to summarize briefly the conservation laws and appropriate expressions for the determination of transport coefficients[1–6].

2.1. CONSERVATION EQUATIONS

The conservation laws for a two-component gas mixture are well known and have been given, for example, by CHAPMAN and COWLING[1]. Generalization of the results to an arbitrary multicomponent mixture can be carried out by determining the invariants arising in the solution of the Boltzmann equation for multicomponent gas mixtures. The results of this study have been published by CURTISS, HIRSCHFELDER *et al*[2,4].

For the study of chemical reactions during flow through a de Laval nozzle, diffusion flames, laminar flame propagation, and the burning of stationary droplets of liquid fuels in an oxidizing atmosphere, only the simplest forms of the equations of motion and of the energy equation are needed. For this reason it is usually most expedient to discuss the relevant expressions in connection with each particular problem treated.

The chemical reaction rates enter explicitly into the continuity equation for each chemical species. We present here a detailed discussion of the continuity equations for reacting multicomponent gas mixtures. In addition, we include the results of VON KÁRMÁN's[3] complete treatment of the equations of motion and of the energy equation.

(*A*) *Definitions and notation*

Useful symbols, definitions, and representative dimensions of physical quantities are the following:

c_K = moles of species K per unit volume (moles of K per cm^3 of mixture);

c_t = total number of moles per unit volume (moles of mixture per cm^3 of mixture);

W_K = molecular weight of species K (grams of K per mole of K);
$\overline{W}$ = molecular weight of the gas mixture (grams of mixture per mole of mixture);
ρ = density of the fluid mixture (grams of mixture per unit volume of mixture);
ρ_K = partial density of species K (grams of K per unit volume of mixture);
$\vec{v}_K$ = flow velocity of species K (cm per sec);
$\vec{v}$ = mass-weighted average velocity of the fluid mixture (cm per sec);
$\vec{V}_K$ = diffusion velocity of species K (cm per sec);
Y_K = weight fraction of species K (grams of K per gram of mixture);
X_K = mole fraction of species K (moles of K per mole of mixture);
γ_K = net molar rate of production of species K per unit volume by chemical reaction (moles of K per cm^3 per sec) $= (\dot{M}_K)$;
w_K = net mass rate of production of species K per unit volume by chemical reaction (grams of K per cm^3 per sec).

It is apparent from the preceding definitions that

$$c_t = \sum_K c_K \qquad \text{.... (2.1)}$$

$$\rho = \sum_K W_K c_K = \sum_K \rho_K \qquad \text{.... (2.2)}$$

$$w_K = W_K \gamma_K \qquad \text{.... (2.3)}$$

$$\overline{W} = \sum_K W_K X_K \qquad \text{.... (2.4)}$$

$$Y_K = \rho_K/\rho = W_K X_K/\overline{W} = W_K X_K/\sum_K W_K X_K \qquad \text{.... (2.5)}$$

$$c_K = \rho Y_K/W_K \qquad \text{.... (2.6)}$$

If the ideal gas law holds, then

$$p = c_t RT = \rho RT/\overline{W} = \rho RT/\sum_K W_K X_K \qquad \text{.... (2.7)}$$

if R represents the molar gas constant.

The mass-weighted average velocity $\vec{v}$ is defined by the relation

$$\vec{v} = \sum_K Y_K \vec{v}_K = (1/\rho) \sum_K \rho_K \vec{v}_K = (1/\rho) \sum_K W_K c_K \vec{v}_K \qquad \text{.... (2.8)}$$

The diffusion velocity $\vec{V}_K$ of species K is the difference between the actual flow velocity of species K and the mass-weighted average velocity, viz.,

$$\vec{v}_K = \vec{v} + \vec{V}_K \qquad \text{.... (2.9)}$$

By replacing $\vec{v}_K$ in Eq. 2.8 according to Eq. 2.9 the following result is obtained:

$$\vec{v} = \sum_K Y_K \vec{v} + \sum_K Y_K \vec{V}_K = \vec{v} + \sum_K Y_K \vec{V}_K$$

whence it follows that

$$\sum_K Y_K \vec{V}_K = \sum_K (\rho_K/\rho) \vec{V}_K = (1/\rho) \sum_K W_K c_K \vec{V}_K = 0 \quad .... \ (2.10)$$

Since mass is neither created nor destroyed by chemical reaction, the following relation must always apply:

$$\sum_K w_K = \sum_K W_K \gamma_K = 0 \quad .... \ (2.11)$$

(*B*) *Continuity equation*

Since the derivation of the conservation equations can be found in standard treatises[1,2,3], and, furthermore, is not essential for the practical applications which we shall consider, it will be sufficient for our purposes to state the results. The basic equations are written either in vectorial form or in cartesian tensor notation. In the latter case the x-, y-, and z-axes are designated as x_l, $l=1$, 2, and 3, respectively; the x-, y-, and z-components of a vector are identified by the subscripts $l=1$, $l=2$, and $l=3$, respectively.

The continuity equation for the K'th chemical species in an n-component mixture can be written in the form

$$\frac{\partial(\rho Y_K)}{\partial t} + \sum_{l=1}^{3} \frac{\partial(\rho Y_K v_{K,l})}{\partial x_l} = w_K, \ K = 1, 2, \ldots n \quad .... \ (2.12)$$

In vectorial form Eq. 2.12 becomes

$$\frac{\partial(\rho Y_K)}{\partial t} + \nabla \cdot (\rho Y_K \vec{v}_K) = w_K, \ K = 1, 2, \ldots n \quad .... \ (2.12a)$$

The overall continuity equation may be obtained from Eq. 2.12 by summing over all of the chemical species. In this manner it is found that

$$\frac{\partial \rho}{\partial t} + \sum_{l=1}^{3} \frac{\partial(\rho v_l)}{\partial x_l} = 0 \quad .... \ (2.13)$$

since $\sum_K Y_K = 1$ and $\sum_K Y_K \vec{v}_K = \vec{v}$. In vectorial notation Eq. 2.13 becomes

$$\frac{\partial \rho}{\partial t} + \nabla \cdot (\rho \vec{v}) = 0 \quad .... \ (2.13a)$$

The Euler total time derivative following the motion of the fluid is defined by the relation

$$\frac{\mathrm{D}}{\mathrm{D}t}=\frac{\partial}{\partial t}+\sum_{l=1}^{3} v_l \frac{\partial}{\partial x_l}$$

or, in vectorial notation,

$$(\mathrm{D}/\mathrm{D}t)=(\partial/\partial t)+\vec{v}\cdot\nabla$$

Hence Eq. 2.13 can be rewritten in the form

$$\frac{\mathrm{D}\rho}{\mathrm{D}t}+\sum_{l=1}^{3}\rho\frac{\partial v_l}{\partial x_l}=0 \qquad \text{.... (2.14)}$$

or, in vectorial notation,

$$\mathrm{D}\rho/\mathrm{D}t+\rho\nabla\cdot\vec{v}=0 \qquad \text{.... (2.14a)}$$

Alternate expressions for the continuity equation can be obtained, for example, by replacing ρY_K in Eq. 2.12 by $c_K\ W_K$ according to Eq. 2.6. In this manner it is found that

$$\frac{\partial c_K}{\partial t}+\sum_{l=1}^{3}\frac{\partial(c_K v_{K,\,l})}{\partial x_l}=w_K/W_K=\gamma_K$$

or

$$\frac{\partial c_K}{\partial t}+\sum_{l=1}^{3}\left[v_l\frac{\partial c_K}{\partial x_l}+\frac{\partial}{\partial x_l}(c_K V_{K,\,l})+c_K\frac{\partial v_l}{\partial x_l}\right]=\gamma_K$$

whence

$$\frac{\mathrm{D}c_K}{\mathrm{D}t}=\sum_{l=1}^{3}\frac{\partial(c_K V_{K,\,l})}{\partial x_l}-\frac{c_K}{\rho}\frac{\mathrm{D}\rho}{\mathrm{D}t}=\gamma_K$$

where use has been made of Eq. 2.14. The last expression can also be written as

$$\frac{\mathrm{D}\ln(c_K/\rho)}{\mathrm{D}t}=\frac{\gamma_K}{c_K}-\frac{1}{c_K}\sum_{l=1}^{3}\frac{\partial(c_K V_{K,\,l})}{\partial x_l}$$

or

$$\frac{\mathrm{D}\ln Y_K}{\mathrm{D}t}=\frac{w_K}{\rho Y_K}-\frac{1}{\rho Y_K}\sum_{l=1}^{3}\frac{\partial(\rho Y_K V_{K,\,l})}{\partial x_l} \qquad \text{.... (2.15)}$$

In vectorial notation Eq. 2.15 becomes

$$\mathrm{D}(\ln Y_K)/\mathrm{D}t=(w_K/\rho Y_K)-(1/\rho Y_K)\nabla\cdot(\rho Y_K\vec{V}_K) \qquad \text{.... (2.15a)}$$

For flow systems with negligible diffusion currents, Eq. 2.15 takes the very simple form

$$\rho(\mathrm{D}Y_K/\mathrm{D}t)=w_K,\ V_{K,\,l}=0$$

which is useful for an analysis of chemical reactions during expansion through a de Laval nozzle.

The chemical source function w_K represents the mass rate of production of species K by chemical reaction and is determined from chemical kinetics. For example, for the reversible chemical reaction

$$\sum_{j=1}^{n} \nu_j' M_j \underset{k_b}{\overset{k_f}{\rightleftarrows}} \sum_{j=1}^{n} \nu_j'' M_j$$

explicit expressions have been given for $(\dot{M}_K)$ in Eq. 1.67, where $\gamma_K \equiv (\dot{M}_K) = w_K/W_K$ is the mole rate of production of species K per unit volume. In view of Eq. 1.67 we find, therefore, that

$$w_K = W_K(\nu_K'' - \nu_K')k_f[1 - (K'/K)]\rho^m \prod_{j=1}^{n} (Y_j/W_j)^{\nu_j'}, \; m = \sum_{j=1}^{n} \nu_j'$$

for the general reversible one-step chemical reaction.

An arbitrary set of p' simultaneous chemical reactions involving n distinct chemical species is described by the following p' stoichiometric relations:

$$\sum_{j=1}^{n} \nu_{j,r}' M_j \xrightarrow{k_r} \sum_{j=1}^{n} \nu_{j,r}'' M_j, \quad r = 1, 2, \ldots p' \quad \ldots. \; (2.16)$$

Here $\nu_{j,r}'$ and $\nu_{j,r}''$ are appropriate stoichiometric coefficients for species j in the r'th chemical process. The chemical source function w_K for the set of p' simultaneous reactions is seen to be

$$w_K = \sum_{r=1}^{p'} w_{K,r}$$

where $w_{K,r}$ is the source function for species K in the r'th reaction, i.e.,

$$w_{K,r} = W_K(\nu_{K,r}'' - \nu_{K,r}')k_r \rho^{m_r} \prod_{j=1}^{n} (Y_j/W_j)^{\nu_{j,r}'}, \; m_r = \sum_{j=1}^{n} \nu_{j,r}'$$

Hence

$$w_K = W_K \sum_{r=1}^{p'} (\nu_{K,r}'' - \nu_{K,r}')k_r \rho^{m_r} \prod_{j=1}^{n} (Y_j/W_j)^{\nu_{j,r}'} \quad \ldots. \; (2.17)$$

for an arbitrary set of p' simultaneous chemical reaction steps.

(C) *Equations of motion*[3]

The equation of motion in reacting gas mixtures is

$$\rho \frac{\partial v_1}{\partial t} + \rho \sum_{l=1}^{3} v_l \frac{\partial v_1}{\partial x_l} = -\frac{\partial p}{\partial x_1} - \rho F_1 + \sum_{l=1}^{3} \frac{\partial(\tau^v{}_{1l} + \tau^D{}_{1l})}{\partial x_l} \quad \ldots. \; (2.18)$$

with similar expressions for the x_2- and x_3-components. The vectorial form of Eq. 2.18 is

$$\rho \frac{\partial \vec{v}}{\partial t} + \rho(\vec{v} \cdot \nabla)\vec{v} = -\nabla p + \rho \vec{F} + \nabla \cdot (\underset{\sim}{\tau}^v + \underset{\sim}{\tau}^D) \quad \ldots. \; (2.18a)$$

Here the components of the viscous stress tensor $\underset{\sim}{\tau}^v$ are given by the relation

$$\tau^{v}_{ij} = -\frac{2}{3}\mu\left(\sum_{l=1}^{3}\frac{\partial v_l}{\partial x_l}\right)\delta_{ij} + \mu\left(\frac{\partial v_i}{\partial x_j} + \frac{\partial v_j}{\partial x_i}\right) \quad \text{.... (2.19)}$$

and the components of the diffusion stress tensor are $\underset{\sim}{\tau}^D$ obtained from expressions of the type:

$$\tau^{D}_{1l} = -\rho\sum_{K=1}^{n} Y_K V_{K,1} V_{K,l} \quad \text{.... (2.20)}$$

Here μ is the viscosity coefficient of the gas, $\delta_{ij}=0$ for $i \neq j$ and $\delta_{ij}=1$ for $i=j$; $\vec{F}$ is an external force acting on unit mass of fluid mixture.

(*D*) *Energy equation*[3]

The complete energy equation can be written in the form

$$\rho\frac{D}{Dt}(e+\tfrac{1}{2}|v|^2) + \rho\frac{D}{Dt}\left(\tfrac{1}{2}\sum_{K=1}^{n} Y_K|V_K|^2\right) =$$
$$-\sum_{l=1}^{3}\frac{\partial(pv_l)}{\partial x_l} + \sum_{l=1}^{3}\frac{\partial}{\partial x_l}\left[\sum_{s=1}^{3} v_s(\tau^v{}_{sl} + \tau^D{}_{sl})\right] + \rho\sum_{l=1}^{3} F_l v_l$$
$$+\sum_{l=1}^{3}\frac{\partial}{\partial x_l}\left(\lambda\frac{\partial T}{\partial x_l}\right) - \sum_{l=1}^{3}\frac{\partial}{\partial x_l}\left(\rho\sum_{K=1}^{n} Y_K h_K V_{K,l}\right)$$
$$-\sum_{l=1}^{3}\frac{\partial}{\partial x_l}\left(\tfrac{1}{2}\rho\sum_{K=1}^{n} Y_K V_{K,l}|V_K|^2\right) \quad \text{.... (2.21)}$$

or, in vectorial form,

$$\rho\frac{D}{Dt}(e+\tfrac{1}{2}|v|^2) + \rho\frac{D}{Dt}\left(\tfrac{1}{2}\sum_{K=1}^{n} Y_K|V_K|^2\right) =$$
$$\nabla\cdot(\vec{pv}) + \nabla\cdot[\vec{v}\cdot(\underset{\sim}{\tau}^v + \underset{\sim}{\tau}^D)] + \nabla\cdot(\lambda\nabla T)$$
$$+\rho(\vec{F}.\vec{v}) - \nabla\cdot\left(\rho\sum_{K=1}^{n} Y_K h_K \vec{V}_K\right) + E' \quad \text{.... (2.22)}$$

where E' represents the term involving the third power of the diffusion velocities. Here e is the specific internal energy of the gas mixture and the other symbols have their usual meaning.

2.2. Transport Properties of Gases

The rates of chemical reactions in flow systems are dependent on mass and energy transport. Except for a few low-velocity flow problems, knowledge of viscosity coefficients is also required for the detailed description of results. For these reasons, the present discussion is devoted to a survey of relevant diffusion equations and of methods for the calculation of transport coefficients in gases.

Theoretical calculations of transport coefficients for gases can be carried out by utilizing the kinetic theory of gases. The results for pure systems and for two-component systems are given in the classical treatise of CHAPMAN and COWLING[1]. Extensions to multicomponent gas mixtures have been published by HIRSCHFELDER and his collaborators[2]. The theoretical studies involve an analytical apparatus of considerable complexity, the detailed description of which is outside the scope of the present discussion. We shall content ourselves with a brief summary of relevant results.

(*A*) *Diffusional properties of gases*

For binary gas mixtures, absolute values for the diffusion velocities are obtained from Eq. 2.10 which becomes

$$Y_1\vec{V}_1 + Y_2\vec{V}_2 = 0 \qquad \text{.... (2.23)}$$

and from the following expression[1]

$$\vec{V}_1 - \vec{V}_2 = -\frac{c_t^2}{c_1c_2}\mathrm{D}_{12}\left[\nabla\left(\frac{c_1}{c_t}\right) + \frac{c_1c_2(W_2 - W_1)}{c_t\rho}\nabla\ln p - \frac{\rho_1\rho_2}{p\rho}(\vec{F}_1 - \vec{F}_2) + k_T\nabla\ln T\right] \qquad \text{.... (2.24)}$$

In Eq. 2.24 the parameter D_{12} is the binary diffusion coefficient for the interdiffusion of species 1 and 2, p equals the pressure, $\vec{F}_K$ is an external force per gram of species K, and $k_T = \mathrm{D}_T/\mathrm{D}_{12}$ is the thermal diffusion ratio if D_T represents the thermal diffusion coefficient. Reference to Eq. 2.24 shows that the difference in the diffusion velocities, $\vec{V}_1 - \vec{V}_2$, has components arising from non-uniformity of composition, of pressure, and of temperature, and another component resulting from the difference in the accelerative effects produced on the two components of the mixture by an external force. For a gas at rest it can be shown[1] that Eq. 2.24 reduces to the expression

$$\vec{V}_1 - \vec{V}_2 = -\frac{c_t^2}{c_1c_2}\mathrm{D}_{12}\left[\nabla\ln p - \frac{\rho_1}{p}\vec{F}_1 + k_T\nabla\ln T\right] \qquad \text{.... (2.25)}$$

VON KÁRMÁN[3] has studied the special cases of concentration diffusion, pressure diffusion, and thermal diffusion. For binary mixtures, in the absence of external forces, his results are summarized by the relations:

$$\vec{V}_1 = -\mathrm{D}_{12}\left[\nabla\ln Y_1 + \left(\frac{Y_1}{W_1} + \frac{Y_2}{W_2}\right)(W_2 - W_1)Y_2\nabla\ln p + \frac{(W_2Y_1 + W_1Y_2)^2}{W_1W_2}\frac{k_T}{Y_1}\nabla\ln T\right] \qquad \text{.... (2.26)}$$

Similarly, it is found that

$$\vec{V}_2 = -\mathrm{D}_{12}\left[\nabla \ln Y_2 + \left(\frac{Y_1}{W_1} + \frac{Y_2}{W_2}\right)(W_1 - W_2) Y_1 \nabla \ln p - \frac{(W_2 Y_1 + W_1 Y_2)^2}{W_1 W_2} \frac{k_T}{Y_2} \nabla \ln T\right] \quad \text{.... (2.27)}$$

The diffusion equations for multicomponent gas mixtures are so complex that it is customary, for the solution of most flow problems with chemical reactions, to use approximate relations for the diffusion velocities and diffusion coefficients. Relevant material has been described by HIRSCHFELDER and his collaborators[2,4], and also by VON KÁRMÁN[3]. Hirschfelder *et al* separate the thermal diffusion effects from concentration and pressure diffusion and from diffusion produced by external forces. They obtain[4] the following relation for an n-component gas mixture:

$$c_i \sum_{j=1}^{n} \frac{c_j}{\mathrm{D}_{ij}} (\vec{V}_{icpF} - \vec{V}_{jcpF}) = -c_t^2 \left[\nabla\left(\frac{c_i}{c_t}\right) + \left(\frac{c_i}{c_t} - \frac{c_i W_i}{\rho}\right) \nabla \ln p - \frac{c_i W_i}{\rho p}\left(\rho \vec{F}_i - \sum_{j=1}^{n} c_j W_j \vec{F}_j\right)\right],\ i \neq j,\ i = 1, 2, \ldots n \quad \text{.... (2.28)}$$

Here the D_{ij} are the ordinary binary diffusion coefficients for inter-diffusion of species i and j; $\vec{V}_{icpF}$ is the diffusion velocity of species i produced by concentration and pressure gradients and by external forces. The thermal diffusion velocity is given by an expression of the form

$$\vec{V}_{iT} = -\mathrm{D}_{iT} \nabla \ln T \quad \text{.... (2.29)}$$

where D_{iT} represents the thermal diffusion coefficient, which can only be calculated[4] with great difficulty.

The numerical values for V_{icpT} are given[3], in first approximation, by the relation

$$\vec{V}_{icpT} = \vec{V}_{ic} + \vec{V}_{ip} + \vec{V}_{iT} \quad \text{.... (2.30)}$$

with $\vec{V}_{iT}$ determined by Eq. 2.29; $\vec{V}_{ic}$ is obtained from the following expressions:

$$\sum_{j=1}^{n} \frac{Y_j}{W_j \mathrm{D}_{ij}} (\vec{V}_{ic} - \vec{V}_{jc}) = \sum_{j=1}^{n} \frac{Y_j}{W_j}\left(\frac{\nabla Y_j}{Y_j} - \frac{\nabla Y_i}{Y_i}\right),\ i \neq j,\ i = 1, 2, \ldots n \quad \text{.... (2.31)}$$

and

$$\sum_{j=1}^{n} Y_j \vec{V}_{jc} = 0 \quad \text{.... (2.32)}$$

Finally, $\vec{V}_{ip}$ can be calculated from the relations

$$\sum_{j=1}^{n} \frac{Y_j}{W_j \mathrm{D}_{ij}} (\vec{V}_{ip} - \vec{V}_{jp}) = -\left(\sum_{j=1}^{n} \frac{Y_j}{W_j}\right)\left(\sum_{j=1}^{n} \frac{Y_j W_j - W_i Y_j}{W_j}\right) \nabla \ln p, i \neq j, \quad i = 1, 2, \ldots n \qquad \text{.... (2.33)}$$

and

$$\sum_{j=1}^{n} Y_j \vec{V}_{jp} = 0 \qquad \text{.... (2.34)}$$

For the diffusion of species i, if i is present as a trace in an n-component gas mixture, CURTISS and HIRSCHFELDER[4] give the following useful relation:

$$c_i W_i \vec{V}_{icpF} = -\frac{c_t^2 W_i \left(1 - \frac{c_i W_i}{\rho}\right)}{\sum_{j \neq i}^{u} \left(\frac{c_j}{\mathrm{D}_{ij}}\right)} \left[\nabla\left(\frac{c_i}{c_t}\right) + \left(\frac{c_i}{c_t} - \frac{c_i W_i}{\rho}\right) \nabla \ln p - \left(\frac{c_i W_i}{\rho p}\right)\left(\rho \vec{F}_i - \sum_{j=1}^{n} c_j W_j \vec{F}_j\right)\right] \qquad \text{.... (2.35)}$$

After introduction of weight fractions, Eq. 2.35 reduces to the result

$$\vec{V}_{icpF} = -\frac{W_i (1 - Y_i) \left[\sum_{j=1}^{n} (Y_j / W_j)\right]^2}{Y_i \sum_{j=1}^{n} (Y_j / W_j \mathrm{D}_{ij})} \left\{ \nabla \left[\frac{(Y_i / W_i)}{\sum_{j=1}^{n} (Y_j / W_j)}\right] + Y_i \left(\frac{1}{\sum_{j=1}^{n} (W_i Y_j / W_j)} - 1\right) \nabla \ln p - \frac{Y_i}{RT} \frac{W_i}{\overline{W}} \left(\vec{F}_i - \sum_{j=1}^{n} Y_j \vec{F}_j\right) \right\} \qquad \text{.... (2.36)}$$

where $\overline{W}$ is the average molecular weight.

(*B*) *Binary diffusion coefficients*

It has been shown in the preceding sections that diffusional transport in gases, except for thermal diffusion, can be calculated from the composition, pressure, and temperature, once the binary diffusion coefficients have been determined. Expressions for the binary diffusion coefficients are obtained[1,2] from the kinetic theory of gases.

Straightforward but laborious calculations[1,2] show how the transport coefficients for monatomic gases can be determined if the interaction potential is known. In practice it is found that the internal motion of molecules if unimportant in mass and momentum transfer. Therefore, the results obtained for monatomic gases can be applied for the determination of diffusion and viscosity coefficients of polyatomic gases. The thermal conductivity of polyatomic gases, on the other hand, cannot be calculated satisfactorily because the internal molecular motion makes an important contribution to this transfer coefficient.

The first approximation to the binary diffusion coefficient D_{12} (in cm^2/sec) for nonpolar gases is independent of the relative concentrations of the two components and is given[2,5] by the relation

$$D_{12} = 2.6280 \times 10^{-3} \frac{\sqrt{T^3(W_1+W_2)/2W_1W_2}}{p\sigma_{12}{}^2\Omega_{12}{}^{(1,1)*}} \quad .... \quad (2.37)$$

In Eq. 2.37 the pressure is given in atmospheres, the temperature in °K, and the molecular weight in g/mole. The parameter σ_{12} (in Å) is a suitably chosen collision diameter for collision between molecules 1

Table 2.1. The parameters ϵ/k and σ determined from viscosity data. (Data of Bird, Hirschfelder, and Curtiss[5]).*

Gas	ϵ/k (°K)	σ (Å)	Gas	ϵ/k (°K)	σ (Å)
Ne	35·7	2·789	AsH_3	281	4·060
	27·5	2·858	HgI_2	698	5·625
A	124	3·418	$HgBr_2$	530	5·414
	116	3·465	$SnBr_4$	465	6·666
Kr	190	3·610	$SnCl_4$	1550	4·540
Xe	229	4·055	Hg	851	2·898
Air	97	3·617	C_2H_2 (acetylene)	185	4·221
	84	3·689	C_2H_4 (ethylene)	205	4·232
N_2	91·5	3·681	C_2H_6 (ethane)	230	4·418
	79·8	3·749	C_3H_8 (propane)	254	5·061
O_2	113	3·433	n-C_4H_{10} (normal butane)	410	4·997
	88	3·541	i-C_4H_{10} (iso-butane)	313	5·341
H_2	(33·3)†	(2·968)	n-C_5H_{12} (normal pentane)	345	5·769
CO	110	3·590	n-C_6H_{14} (normal hexane)	413	5·909
	88	3·706	n-C_7H_{16} (normal heptane)	(282)	(8·88)
CO_2	190	3·996	n-C_8H_{18} (normal octane)	320	7·451
	213	3·897	n-C_9H_{20} (normal nonane)	240	8·448
NO	119	3·470	C_6H_{12} (cyclohexane)	324	6·093
	91	3·599	C_6H_6 (benzene)	440	5·270
N_2O	220	3·879	CH_3OH	507	3·585
	237	3·816	C_2H_5OH	391	4·455
CH_4	137	3·882	CH_3Cl	855	3·375
	144	3·796	CH_2Cl_2	406	4·759
CF_4	(152·5)	(4·70)	$CHCl_3$	427	5·430
CCl_4	327	5·881	C_2N_2	339	4·380
SO_2	252	4.290	COS	335	4·130
SF_6	(201)	(5·51)	CS_2	488	4·438
F_2	112	3·653			
Cl_2	357	4·115			
	257	4·400			
Br_2	520	4·268			
I_2	550	4·982			
HCl	360	3·305			
HI	324	4·123			

* Multiple entries refer to results deduced from different experimental measurements[5].

† Values in parentheses were obtained from equation-of-state data and are given only if no results based on viscosity measurements are available.

and 2, and $\Omega_{12}^{(1,1)*}$ is a dimensionless double integral whose value depends on the dynamics of binary collisions and, therefore, on the intermolecular force law.

For a pure nonpolar gas the intermolecular potential $\phi(r)$ as a function of the distance r between molecular centers is given, approximately, by the relation

$$\phi(r) = 4\epsilon_i\left[\left(\frac{\sigma_i}{r}\right)^{12} - \left(\frac{\sigma_i}{r}\right)^{6}\right] \quad .... \ (2.38)$$

where the energy ϵ_i and the length σ_i are characteristics of the i'th molecular species. For mixtures of nonpolar gases the following expressions may be used:

$$\sigma_{12} = \tfrac{1}{2}(\sigma_1 + \sigma_2), \ \epsilon_{12} = \sqrt{\epsilon_1 \epsilon_2} \quad .... \ (2.39)$$

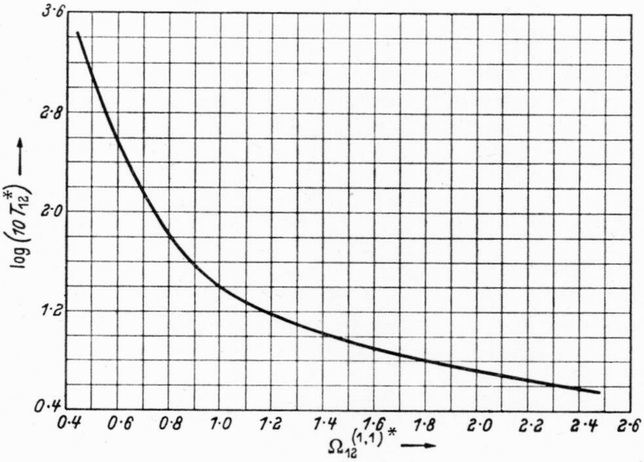

Fig. 2.1. The collision integrals $\Omega_{12}^{(1,1)*}$ *as a function of log* $(10T_{12}^*)$. *Based on the data of Bird, Hirschfelder, and Curtiss*[5].

Numerical values of ϵ_1 and σ_1 for a number of molecules are summarized in *Table 2.1*[5]. The collision integral depends on the parameter

$$T_{12}^* = kT/\epsilon_{12}$$

and is plotted[5] in *Fig. 2.1* as a function of log $(10T_{12}^*)$.

Binary diffusion coefficients calculated by the use of Eq. 2.37 have been found to be reliable within a few per cent for the temperature ranges for which experimental data are available. For the analysis of problems involving chemical reactions in flow systems it is frequently important to estimate the temperature and pressure dependence of diffusion coefficients. For this purpose it is reasonable to use the rule

$$D_{12} = D_{12}^{\circ}\ (T/T^{\circ})^{\nu}\ (p^{\circ}/p),\ 1.5 \leqslant \nu \leqslant 2 \quad .... \ (2.40)$$

Additional information concerning the calculation of diffusion coefficients may be found in the original literature[1,2,5].

(C) *Thermal diffusion coefficients*

The thermal diffusion coefficient D_T is given in terms of D_{12} and the thermal diffusion ratio k_T by the expression

$$D_T = k_T D_{12} \qquad \text{.... (2.41)}$$

Approximate methods for the calculation of k_T, which is a sensitive function of composition, are given in the literature. As the temperature is lowered, k_T decreases for many pairs of gases. For mixtures of hydrogen and nitrogen at 0° K, k_T increases from 0 to about 0·09 as the percentage of hydrogen is increased from 0 to 60 per cent; for larger concentrations of hydrogen, k_T decreases again.

(D) *Viscosity coefficients of gases*

The viscosity coefficients, μ, can be calculated, in good approximation, from the kinetic theory of gases[1,2,5]. For the pure nonpolar gas i the first approximation to the viscosity coefficient is

$$\mu_i = 2{\cdot}67 \times 10^{-5} \frac{\sqrt{W_i T}}{\sigma_i^2 \Omega_i^{(2,2)*}} \qquad \text{.... (2.42)}$$

where μ_i is expressed in g/cm × sec, W_i is the molecular weight of species i in g/mole, T is the absolute temperature in °K, σ_i is the collision diameter for collisions between species i and species i in Å, and $\Omega_i^{(2,2)*}$ is a collision integral which depends on the parameter

$$T_i^* = kT/\epsilon_i$$

The collision integral $\Omega_i^{(2,2)*}$ is plotted as a function of log $(10T_i^*)$ in *Fig. 2.2.*

A useful empirical equation[6] for the viscosity, μ_{mix}, of a multicomponent gas mixture is the following:

$$\mu_{\text{mix}} = \sum_{i=1}^{n} \frac{X_i^2}{\dfrac{X_i^2}{\mu_i} + 1{\cdot}385 \displaystyle\sum_{j=1,\, j\neq i}^{n} (X_i X_j RT/pW_i D_{ij})} \qquad \text{.... (2.43)}$$

Here D_{ij} is the binary diffusion coefficient discussed in Sec. 2*B*, and X_m denotes, as usual, the mole fraction of species m.

(E) *Thermal conductivities of gases*

For the pure monatomic gas i the first approximation to the thermal conductivity is given by the relation

$$\lambda_i = 1{\cdot}99 \times 10^{-4} \frac{\sqrt{T/W_i}}{\sigma_i^2 \Omega_i^{(2,2)*}} = \frac{15}{4} \frac{R}{W_i} \mu_i \qquad \text{.... (2.44)}$$

where λ_i is expressed in cal/cm × sec × °K and the other symbols have their usual meaning.

For a pure polyatomic gas the following approximate relation may be used for the thermal conductivity:

$$\lambda_i \simeq \frac{15}{4}\frac{R}{W_i}\mu_i\left(\frac{4}{15}\frac{C_{vi}}{R}+\frac{3}{5}\right) \qquad \text{.... (2.45)}$$

In Eq. 2.44, C_{vi} is the molar heat capacity at constant volume for species i. The factor in parentheses is known as the Eucken approximation and takes into account, approximately, the transfer of energy between

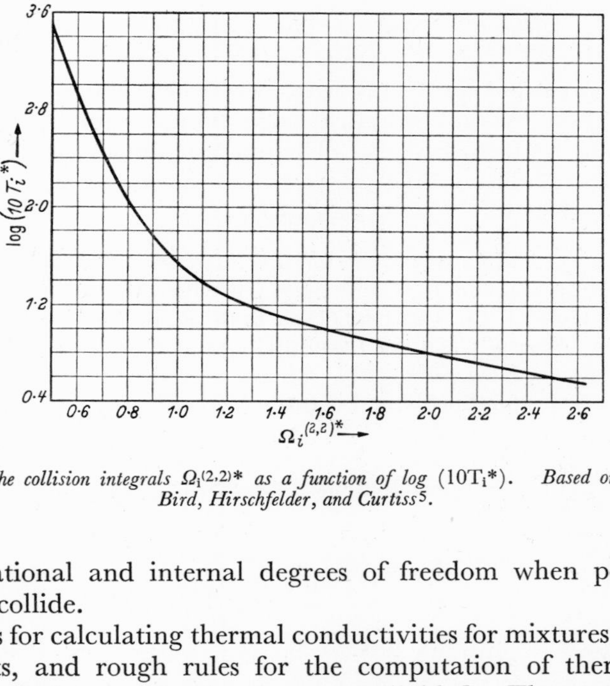

Fig. 2.2. The collision integrals $\Omega_i^{(2,2)*}$ as a function of log $(10T_i^*)$. *Based on the data of Bird, Hirschfelder, and Curtiss*[5].

the translational and internal degrees of freedom when polyatomic molecules collide.

Methods for calculating thermal conductivities for mixtures of atomic constituents, and rough rules for the computation of thermal conductivities of mixtures of molecules, are available[5]. These calculations are laborious and usually not very reliable because of the uncertain energy transfer between translational and internal degrees of freedom. For this reason it is recommended that thermal conductivities for gas mixtures be estimated, wherever possible, by the use of empirical data.

For two-component mixtures, with large differences in the thermal conductivity between the two components, the following rule yields useful approximations:

$$\lambda_{\text{mix}} = \tfrac{1}{2}\left[(\lambda_1 X_1 + \lambda_2 X_2) + \frac{\lambda_1\lambda_2}{(X_1\sqrt{\lambda_2}+X_2\sqrt{\lambda_1})^2}\right] \qquad \text{.... (2.46)}$$

For binary mixtures, with similar thermal conductivities for the two chemical species (e.g., isotopic mixtures), the following rule may be used:

$$\frac{1}{\sqrt{\lambda_{\text{mix}}}}=\frac{\sqrt{X_1}}{\lambda_1}+\frac{\sqrt{X_2}}{\lambda_2} \quad \text{.... (2.47)}$$

In the analysis of flow problems with chemical reactions it is customary to assume that the thermal conductivity is independent of pressure and varies at T^{ν} with $\frac{1}{2}\leqslant\nu\leqslant 1$.

(F) Other parameters derivable from the kinetic theory of gases

The kinetic theory of gases also provides methods for estimating (a) Joule–Thomson coefficients and (b) corrections to the ideal gas equation of state[1,2,5]. Since the ideal gas law is usually an adequate approximation and since Joule–Thomson coefficients do not usually enter into the analysis of flow problems with chemical reactions, we shall not discuss methods for the theoretical calculation of equations of state and of Joule–Thomson coefficients. The interested reader is referred to the literature for details.

REFERENCES

1 Chapman, S., and Cowling, T. G., *The Mathematical Theory of Nonuniform Gases*, Chapters 8 and 14, Cambridge Univ. Pr., Cambridge, 1939

2 Hirschfelder, J. O., Curtiss, C. F., Bird, R. B., and Spotz, E. L., *The Molecular Theory of Gases and Liquids*, Chapters 3, 4, 8 and 9, John Wiley and Sons, Inc., New York, 1954

3 Kármán, Th. von, Sorbonne Lectures, 1951–52

4 Curtiss, C. F., and Hirschfelder, J. O., *J. chem. Phys.* 17 (1949) 550–555

5 Bird, R. B., Hirschfelder, J. O., and Curtiss, C. F., paper presented before the Heat Transfer Division of the ASME, November 29–December 4, 1953, New York

6 Buddenberg, J. W., and Wilke, C. R., *Industr. Engng Chem.* 41 (1949) 1345–47

CHAPTER 3

CHEMICAL REACTIONS DURING ADIABATIC EXPANSION THROUGH A DE LAVAL NOZZLE*

THE problem of chemical reactions during adiabatic expansion through a de Laval nozzle will be formulated in a general manner. However, actual calculations are outlined only for the case in which the chemical kinetics is described by a single rate-controlling reaction step or by two opposing chemical reactions. In view of our present lack of knowledge of detailed chemical kinetics data, the loss in generality will probably not restrict the utility of the results.

The validity of the ideal gas law is assumed throughout the discussion. Rate laws based on experimental measurements carried out in homogeneous, isothermal, static systems, constructed under the local conditions of temperature, pressure, and concentrations existing in the flow system, will be used.

Two linearized treatments for the study of chemical changes during adiabatic expansion through a de Laval nozzle are presented. The first treatment permits a straightforward calculation of the departure from equilibrium for chemical reactions which occur sufficiently rapidly to approximate the local equilibrium conditions at all times (near-equilibrium flow criteria, Sec. 3.1). The second treatment is useful for a study of chemical reactions which occur so slowly that they produce only small concentration changes during flow (near-frozen flow criteria, Sec. 3.2). Representative applications of the near-equilibrium and near-frozen flow criteria to propellant systems are described in Sec. 3.3. The relation between the extent of chemical reaction during nozzle flow and optimum nozzle design is discussed in Sec. 3.4. Finally, convergence requirements for the flow criteria are examined in Sec. 3.5 and cooling rates for a representative nozzle are determined in Sec. 3.6. The use of the high cooling rates obtainable in a de Laval nozzle for the production of chemical compounds is considered briefly in Sec. 3.7.

The analysis of chemical reactions during one-dimensional nozzle flow is simplified greatly by noting that concentration changes produced by diffusion currents may be neglected because of the large translational velocity of the gases. Furthermore, the rate of change of temperature with time is not a sensitive function of the extent of chemical reaction. Hence a first approximation to the temperature-time history during adiabatic expansion is obtained by utilizing relations appropriate for

* Based, in part, on Tech. Rep. No. 1, Contr. DA 04-495-Ord-446, Office of Ordnance Research, U.S. Army, Calif. Inst. Tech., May 1953.

adiabatic expansion under equilibrium conditions (for near-equilibrium flow) or adiabatic expansion for a gas mixture without composition change (for near-frozen flow). Once the temperature-time history of the expanding gases is known, the extent of chemical reaction can be analyzed by using only the appropriate continuity equation.

3.1. Adiabatic Expansion with Near-Equilibrium Flow[1]

For one-dimensional flow with negligible diffusion currents Eq. 2.15 for species i becomes

$$\mathrm{D}\ln Y_i/\mathrm{D}t = (\mathrm{d}\ln Y_i/\mathrm{d}T)(\mathrm{D}T/\mathrm{D}t) = w_i/\rho Y_i = (\dot{M}_i)/(M_i)$$

or

$$(\mathrm{d}\ln Y_i/\mathrm{d}T) = \frac{W_i}{\rho Y_i}(\dot{M}_i)(\mathrm{D}T/\mathrm{D}t)^{-1} \qquad \ldots. \ (3.1)$$

since $1/(M_i) = W_i/\rho Y_i$. Replacing $(\dot{M}_i)$ in Eq. 3.1 according to the last relation given in Eq. 1.67 leads to the result

$$(\mathrm{d}\ln Y_i/\mathrm{d}T) = (\mathrm{D}T/\mathrm{D}t)^{-1}[(\nu_i'' - \nu_i')W_i/Y_i]k_f[1-(K'/K)] \rho^{m-1}\left[\prod_{j=1}^{n}(Y_j/W_j)^{\nu_j'}\right] \qquad \ldots. \ (3.2)$$

for the general chemical reaction

$$\sum_{j=1}^{n}\nu_j' M_j \underset{k_b}{\overset{k_f}{\rightleftarrows}} \sum_{j=1}^{n}\nu_j'' M_j,\ m = \sum_{j=1}^{n}\nu_j' \qquad \ldots. \ (3.3)$$

Multiplying Eq. 3.2 by $\nu_i'' - \nu_i'$ and summing over all of the available chemical species leads to the relation

$$\sum_{i=1}^{n}(\nu_i'' - \nu_i')(\mathrm{d}\ln Y_i/\mathrm{d}T) = (\mathrm{D}T/\mathrm{D}t)^{-1}k_f\rho^{m-1}\left[\prod_{j=1}^{n}(Y_j/W_j)^{\nu_j'}\right] \left[\sum_{i=1}^{n}(\nu_i'' - \nu_i')^2(W_i/Y_i)\right][1-(K'/K)] \qquad \ldots. \ (3.4)$$

Equation 3.4 is the basic relation from which near-equilibrium flow as well as near-frozen flow criteria may be derived.

The equilibrium constant K_Y has been defined in Chapter 1 by the relation

$$K_Y = \prod_{i=1}^{n}(Y_{i,e})^{(\nu_i'' - \nu_i')} \qquad \ldots. \ (3.5)$$

whereas the corresponding quotient of weight fractions is

$$K_Y' = \prod_{i=1}^{n} Y_i^{(\nu_i'' - \nu_i')} \qquad \ldots. \ (3.6)$$

The intuitive meaning attached to 'near-equilibrium flow' is that the difference between the actual weight fractions, Y_i, and the equilibrium weight fractions for the local conditions of temperature and pressure, $Y_{i,e}$, is not large. In general, the quantity K_Y' may then be considered to be an equilibrium constant at a temperature T' which differs slightly from the actual value of the local temperature T. More precisely, we define near-equilibrium flow as flow for which $T' - T$ is so small that it is sufficient to retain only the first two terms in the Taylor series expansion of $K_Y' = K_Y(T')$ about the temperature T, i.e., for near-equilibrium flow,

$$K_Y' = K_Y(T') \simeq K_Y(T) + K_Y(T)[\mathrm{d}\ln K_Y(T)/\mathrm{d}T]_T(T' - T) \quad \text{.... (3.7)}$$

where the subscript T to the square bracket indicates that the temperature derivative of $\ln K_Y$ is to be evaluated at the local temperature T.* If the expression given in Eq. 3.7 is applied, for example, to the dissociation of hydrogen molecules,

$$X' + H_2 \rightleftarrows 2H + X'$$

then it is clear that the weight fraction of the products of reaction decreases as the temperature is lowered whereas the weight fraction of H_2 increases. Hence the coefficient $\mathrm{d}K_Y/\mathrm{d}T$ is positive and $K_Y(T') \geqslant K_Y(T)$ or $T' \geqslant T$. Similar observations can be made for other chemical reactions.

The summation appearing on the left-hand side of Eq. 3.4 evidently represents the coefficient $[\mathrm{d}\ln K_Y(T')/\mathrm{d}T]_T$. Using Eq. 3.7 it is readily shown that for use on the left-hand side of Eq. 3.4 an adequate zeroth-order approximation is

$$[\mathrm{d}\ln K_Y(T')/\mathrm{d}T]_T \simeq [\mathrm{d}\ln K_Y(T)/\mathrm{d}T]_T \quad \text{.... (3.8)}$$

From Eq. 3.4, 3.7, and 3.8 it now follows that, for near-equilibrium flow,

$$(\mathrm{d}\ln K_Y/\mathrm{d}T)_T \simeq (-\mathrm{D}T/\mathrm{D}t)^{-1} k_f \rho^{m-1} \left[\prod_{j=1}^{n} (Y_j/W_j)^{\nu_j'}\right] \times \left[\sum_{i=1}^{n} (\nu_i'' - \nu_i')^2 W_i/Y_i\right] (\mathrm{d}\ln K_Y/\mathrm{d}T)_T (T' - T)$$

$$= (-\mathrm{D}T/\mathrm{D}t)^{-1} (z)^{-1} (\mathrm{d}\ln K_Y/\mathrm{d}T)_T (T' - T)$$

or

$$T' - T \simeq (-\mathrm{D}T/\mathrm{D}t) z \quad \text{.... (3.9)}$$

* It should be noted that the definition for near-equilibrium flow given in Eq. 3.7 is not generally identical with a similar relation in which K_Y' is replaced by K_c' and K_Y by K_c. However, if the concentration changes produced by a change of state during adiabatic expansion are negligibly small compared to composition changes produced by chemical reactions, then the two definitions of near-equilibrium flow are equivalent for practical purposes. This equivalence has been established in several cases (compare Sec. 3.3 and the references cited therein.).

where z denotes the reaction time, i.e.,

$$z=\left\{k_f\rho^{m-1}\left[\prod_{j=1}^{n}(Y_j/W_j)^{\nu_j'}\right]\left[\sum_{i=1}^{n}(\nu_i''-\nu_i')^2W_i/Y_i\right]\right\}^{-1} \quad .... \ (3.10)$$

It is evident from Eq. 3.9 that the temperature lag $(T'-T)$ is directly proportional to the rate of change of temperature with time for the flowing system and is also proportional to the reaction time z.

Equation 3.9 constitutes the desired result and can be used to obtain approximate estimates for the temperature lag $(T'-T)$ for near-equilibrium flow. As a very crude approximation we may apply Eq. 3.9 to the entire expansion process from chamber temperature T_c to the temperature at the nozzle throat T_t and again between nozzle throat temperature T_t and exit temperature T_e. If the residence time

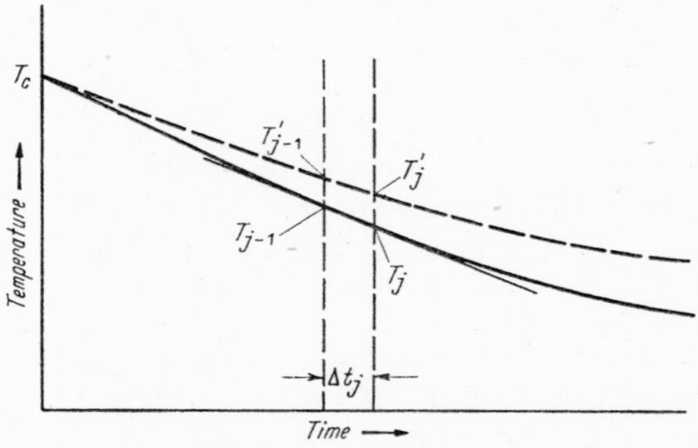

Fig. 3.1. Schematic representation of temperature-time and temperature lag-time plots

n the nozzle is t_t between T_c and T_t and t_r-t_t between T_t and T_e, then it follows from Eq. 3.9 that

$$(T'-T)_1/(T_c-T_t) \sim z/t_t \text{ and } (T'-T)_2/(T_t-T_e) \sim z/(t_r-t_t)$$

as a first and very rough estimate, where the subscripts 1 and 2 refer to the converging and diverging sections, respectively. In order to obtain a conservative near-equilibrium flow criterion it is appropriate to choose such conditions that the reaction time assumes a maximum value, z_{max}. If under these conditions $(t_t)^{-1}z_{max}$, $(t_r-t_t)^{-1}z_{max} \leqslant 10^{-3}$ it is clear that $(T'-T)$ will be negligibly small for the entire expansion process and near-equilibrium flow obtains. Numerical examples will be discussed in Sec. 3.3.

A more accurate temperature lag versus time profile can be constructed by using an iterative procedure for adiabatic expansion through a nozzle. For example, the gas cools from the chamber temperature T_c to the temperature at the nozzle throat T_t during the residence time t_t (*Fig. 3.1*).

We may subdivide the time axis into a series of conveniently chosen time intervals $\Delta t_1, \Delta t_2, \ldots \Delta t_n$. At the beginning of the Δt_j'th time interval the actual composition of the gas mixture corresponds to an 'equilibrium temperature' T'_{j-1}. In order to obtain the 'temperature' T_j' we use Eq. 3.9 with $(-\mathrm{D}T/\mathrm{D}t) = (-\mathrm{D}T/\mathrm{D}t)_j$ corresponding to the average slope in the j'th time interval, Y_j being roughly the weight fraction of j which is characteristic of equilibrium at the temperature T_{j-1}, $T \equiv T'_{j-1}$, and $T' = T_j'$. In this manner the quantity $T_j' - T'_{j-1}$ can be obtained without difficulty and hence the entire 'effective temperature' versus time curve may be constructed. In view of our lack of knowledge concerning more than the order of magnitude of the rate constants involved, a first order approximation to $\mathrm{D}T/\mathrm{D}t$, using adiabatic expansion with complete chemical equilibrium during flow*, is more than adequate. In fact, for most applications the assumption of a constant average value of $-\mathrm{D}T/\mathrm{D}t$, which depends only on T_c, chamber pressure p_c, heat capacity ratio γ, and nozzle dimensions, is sufficient.

3.2. Adiabatic Expansion with Near-Frozen Flow[1]

For a near-frozen flow analysis we start again with Eq. 3.4 but replace Eq. 3.7 by the expression

$$K_Y' = K_Y(T') \simeq K_Y(T_c) - K_Y(T_c)[\mathrm{d}\ln K_Y(T)/\mathrm{d}T]_{T_c}(T_c - T') \quad \ldots. \ (3.11)$$

i.e., near-frozen flow is defined as flow for which the extent of chemical reaction is so small that the difference $T_c - T'$ always remains small. If $\mathrm{d}K_Y/\mathrm{d}T$ is positive then $K_Y(T') \leqslant K_Y(T_c)$ and $T' \leqslant T_c$; if $\mathrm{d}K_Y/\mathrm{d}T$ is negative, then $K_Y(T') \geqslant K_Y(T_c)$ and again $T' \leqslant T_c$.

Using Eq. 3.4 and 3.11 we obtain

$$\sum_{i=1}^{n}(\nu_i'' - \nu_i')(\mathrm{d}\ln Y_i/\mathrm{d}T)_T = (\mathrm{D}T/\mathrm{D}t)^{-1}(z)^{-1}$$
$$\times\{1 - [K_Y(T_c)/K_Y(T)][1 - (\mathrm{d}\ln K_Y/\mathrm{d}T)_{T_c}(T_c - T')]\} \quad \ldots. \ (3.12)$$

It is now necessary to examine with some care the left-hand side of Eq. 3.12, which represents the coefficient $[\mathrm{d}\ln K_Y(T')/\mathrm{d}T]_T$ where $T' \simeq T_c$. Using the approximation given in Eq. 3.11 for near-frozen flow it follows that $[\mathrm{d}\ln K_Y(T')/\mathrm{d}T]_T \simeq [\mathrm{d}\ln K_Y(T)/\mathrm{d}T]_{T_c}\ (\mathrm{d}T'/\mathrm{d}T)$ whence Eq. 3.12 becomes

$$(\mathrm{d}\ln K_Y/\mathrm{d}T)_{T_c}[(T_c - T')/(T_c - T)] \simeq (\mathrm{D}T/\mathrm{D}t)^{-1}(z)^{-1}\{1 - [K_Y(T_c)/K_Y(T)]$$
$$\times[1 - (\mathrm{d}\ln K_Y/\mathrm{d}T)_{T_c}(T_c - T')]\} \quad \ldots. \ (3.13)$$

where it has been assumed, as a zeroth-order approximation, that T' decreases linearly with T. If the kinetics data are sufficiently accurate

* Temperature vs. time profiles have been given, for example, by Penner and Altman[2].

to warrant a more detailed analysis, then the coefficient dT'/dT can be determined by using a straightforward iteration procedure. Equation 3.13 can be solved for the reduced temperature ratio, $(T_c - T')/(T_c - T)$, with the result

$$(T_c - T')/(T_c - T) \simeq (-DT/Dt)^{-1}(z)^{-1} \times [(d\ln K_Y/dT)_{T_c}]^{-1}\{[K_Y(T_c)/K_Y(T)] - 1\} \times \{1 + (T_c - T)[K_Y(T_c)/K_Y(T)](-DT/Dt)^{-1}(z)^{-1}\}^{-1} \quad .... \ (3.14)$$

Conservative near-frozen flow criteria may be obtained from Eq. 3.14 by minimizing the denominator on the right-hand side, thereby obtaining upper limits for $(T_c - T')/(T_c - T)$. In this manner the following interesting pair of results is obtained:

$$(T_c - T')/(T_c - T) \leqslant [-(d\ln K_Y/dT)_{T_c}]^{-1}(T_c - T)^{-1} [K_Y(T)/K_Y(T_c) - 1] \quad .... \ (3.14a)$$

or

$$(T_c - T')/(T_c - T) \leqslant (-DT/Dt)^{-1}(z)^{-1}[1 - K_Y(T_c)/K_Y(T)] [-(d\ln K_Y/dT)_{T_c}]^{-1} \quad .... \ (3.14b)$$

Reference to Eq. 3.14a shows that we have determined an upper limit for the reduced temperature lag $(T_c - T')/(T_c - T)$, which is independent of the reaction time z. Actually Eq. 3.14a may not be useful since the upper limit for $(T_c - T')/(T_c - T)$ determined from Eq. 3.14a may be so large as to invalidate the Taylor series expansion introduced through Eq. 3.11. On the other hand, Eq. 3.14b is useful for slow chemical reactions (large values of z) or for very high rates of cooling (large values of $-DT/Dt$).

An explicit relation in terms of T_c and of the heat of reaction at T_c, ΔH_c, can be obtained by using the general thermodynamic relation (cf. Eq. 1.63)

$$(d\ln K_Y/dT)_{T_c} = (d\ln K_p/dT)_{T_c} - \Delta n(d\ln\rho/dT)_{T_c} - (\Delta n/T) = (\Delta H_c/RT_c^2)\{1 - \Delta n(RT_c^2/\Delta H_c)[(d\ln\rho/dT)_{T_c} + (1/T)]\} \quad .... \ (3.15)$$

where Δn vanishes for chemical reactions in which the total number of moles remains unchanged and $(d\ln\rho/dT)_{T_c} = [T_c(\gamma - 1)]^{-1}$ for adiabatic expansions. For $\Delta n = 0$, Eq. 3.14a becomes

$$(T_c - T')/(T_c - T) \leqslant [RT_c^2/(-\Delta H_c)(T_c - T)]\{[K_Y(T)/K_Y(T_c)] - 1\}$$

But for typical atomic recombination reactions $T_c \sim 3000°K$, $-\Delta H_c \sim 30$ Kcals/mole, and $K_Y(T)/K_Y(T_c) \gg 1$ for T appreciably smaller than T_c. Hence it follows that for $T_c - T \sim 500°K$ the upper limit for the reduced temperature lag calculated from Eq. 3.14a is of the order of unity, i.e., the upper limit which has been calculated does not provide a useful restriction on the magnitude of $(T_c - T')/(T_c - T)$. Application of Eq. 3.14b to specific chemical reactions frequently leads to meaningful restrictions on the ratio $(T_c - T')/(T_c - T)$.

3.3. Application of Flow Criteria to Representative Chemical Reactions

Applications of the near-equilibrium criteria to specific chemical reactions have been described in the literature [3,4]. The use of the conservative near-frozen flow criterion given in Eq. 3.14b is also straightforward. For this reason we shall present only a brief outline of representative calculations.

(*A*) *Recombination of hydrogen atoms**

For the reaction

$$2H + X' \rightarrow H_2 + X' \qquad \text{.... (3.16)}$$

the near-equilibrium criterion given in Eq. 3.9 becomes

$$T' - T \simeq (-\mathrm{D}T/\mathrm{D}t)\{k_f \rho^2 (Y_H/W_H)^2 (Y_{X'}/W_{X'}) [(4W_H/Y_H) + (W_{H_2}/Y_{H_2})]\}^{-1} \qquad \text{.... (3.17)}$$

In comparing the present calculations with those published previously [3] it should be noted that Eq. 3.17 was obtained by defining near-equilibrium flow through Eq. 3.7 rather than by the corresponding relation in which K_Y is replaced by K_c and K_Y' by K_c'. However, for the reaction described by Eq. 3.16 it has been demonstrated that concentration changes associated with a change of state are negligibly small [3]. Hence Eq. 3.17 is practically equivalent to the usual form of the near-equilibrium criterion [3,4]. In terms of concentrations, Eq. 3.17 becomes

$$T' - T \simeq (-\mathrm{D}T/\mathrm{D}t)\{k_f (X')[4(H) + (H)^2/(H_2)]\}^{-1} \qquad \text{... (3.17a)}$$

It is now convenient to utilize Eq. 3.17a in such a manner as to determine the minimum concentration (H) which will lead to near-equilibrium flow for representative de Laval nozzles, i.e., representative values of $(-\mathrm{D}T/\mathrm{D}t)$.

For atomic recombinations as the result of triple collisions, k_f is of the order† of 10^{11} liter^2-sec^{-1}-mole^{-2} at 3000°K. In view of the uncertainties in k_f, the most elaborate form of Eq. 3.17a which is warranted for application is

$$(T' - T)/(T_c - T_e) = t_r^{-1}\{k_f (X')[4(H) + (H)^2/(H_2)]\}^{-1}$$

where t_r represents the residence time in the nozzle. For representative nozzles in 1000 psia thrust chambers it has been shown that $(-\mathrm{D}T/\mathrm{D}t)$

* The recombination of hydrogen atoms was first examined by the use of near-equilibrium flow criteria in reference 3. Following the work described in references 2a and 3, Krieger has carried out an exact numerical solution, which has been published in *J. Amer. Rocket Soc.* 21 (1952) 179.

† The values of k_f have been measured only at low pressures and for a limited number of species X' as third body. The assumptions that similar rate constants can be used in gas mixtures at elevated pressures, and that the activation energy for the recombination of atoms is zero, are questionable and justified only by the lack of better data. [5]

$\simeq(T_c - T_e)/t_r \simeq 3 \times 10^7$ °K-sec^{-1}. The expansion process will correspond to equilibrium flow, for practical purposes, if $T' - T \leqslant 20°$ K whence it follows that near-equilibrium flow will obtain if, conservatively,

$$(H) \geqslant 4 \times 10^5 [k_f(X')]^{-1} \text{ moles/liter}$$

In order to minimize (H) further we use the largest values for both (X') and k_f; thus for (X') we use the value corresponding to the nozzle exit position, i.e., to $T \simeq 2000$°K and $p = 1$ atm. Hence

$$(X') \leqslant (RT)^{-1} = 6{\cdot}1 \times 10^{-3} \text{ moles/liter}$$

similarly

$$k_f \leqslant 7 \times 10^{10} \text{ liter}^2 - \text{sec}^{-1} - \text{mole}^{-2}$$

Use of the listed numerical values leads to the following conservative near-equilibrium criterion for (H) if $-\mathrm{D}T/\mathrm{D}t = 3 \times 10^7$ °K/sec: $(H) \geqslant 9 \times 10^{-4}$ moles/liter. A more detailed study shows that the preceding condition can be relaxed to

$(H) \geqslant 3 \times 10^{-4}$ moles/liter for near-equilibrium flow if

$$(-\mathrm{D}T/\mathrm{D}t) \simeq 3 \times 10^7 \text{ °K/sec} \quad \text{.... (3.18)}$$

This result is useful since it permits an immediate conclusion regarding conditions during nozzle flow for hot propellant systems with sizeable concentrations of hydrogen atoms.

The statement that near-equilibrium flow obtains for $(H) \geqslant 3 \times 10^{-4}$ moles/liter can be supplemented profitably by using the near-frozen flow criterion given in Eq. 3.14. For the case under discussion

$$\begin{aligned}(T_c - T')/(T_c - T) \simeq & (-\mathrm{D}T/\mathrm{D}t)^{-1} k_f(X')[4(H) + (H)^2/(H_2)] \\ & \times [-(\mathrm{dln}K_Y/\mathrm{d}T)_{T_c}]^{-1}\{1 - [K_Y(T_c)/K_Y(T)]\} \\ & \times \{1 + (T_c - T)[K_Y(T_c)/K_Y(T)](-\mathrm{D}T/\mathrm{D}t)^{-1}k_f(X') \\ & [4(H) + (H)^2/(H_2)]\}^{-1} \quad \text{.... (3.19)}\end{aligned}$$

But according to Eq. 3.15,

$$(\mathrm{dln}K_Y/\mathrm{d}T)_{T_c} = \Delta H_c/RT_c^2 + [\gamma/T_c(\gamma - 1)]^{-1} \quad \text{.... (3.20)}$$

where ΔH_c represents the enthalpy change on reaction, for the process described by Eq. 3.16, at the temperature T_c. For the reaction under discussion $-\Delta H_c/RT_c^2 \simeq 10^5/2 \times (3000)^2 = 5{\cdot}6 \times 10^{-3}$ at 3000° K, $[\gamma/T_c(\gamma-1)]^{-1} \simeq 2{\cdot}0 \times 10^{-3}$(°K)$^{-1}$ and $(-\mathrm{dln}K_Y/\mathrm{d}T)_{T_c} \simeq 4 \times 10^{-3}$ (°K)$^{-1}$; also, at $p_c = 20$ atm., $(X') = 20/RT = 8{\cdot}23 \times 10^{-2}$ mole/liter whence $k_f(X') \leqslant 8 \times 10^9$ liter-sec^{-1}-mole^{-1}. For $(-\mathrm{D}T/\mathrm{D}t) \simeq 3 \times 10^7$ (°K/sec) it is found that*

$$[(T_c - T')/(T_c - T)] \leqslant 3 \times 10^5[(H) + (H)^2/4(H_2)][1 - K_Y(T_c)/K_Y(T)]$$

For significant departures of T from T_c, $K_Y(T_c)/K_Y(T) \ll 1$ and the conservative relation

$$(T_c - T')/(T_c - T) \leqslant 3 \times 10^5(H)$$

* A quantitative study of one-dimensional nozzle flow shows that the coefficient $(-\mathrm{D}T/\mathrm{D}t)$ increases very rapidly in the vicinity of the nozzle entrance position. For details see Sec. 3.6.

is obtained. If near-frozen flow obtains for $(T_c - T')/(T_c - T) \leqslant 10^{-2}$, then a sufficient condition to assure the absence of appreciable chemical reaction is $(H) \leqslant 3 \times 10^{-8}$ moles/liter. A more detailed study again shows that this condition can be relaxed somewhat and

$(H) \leqslant 10^{-7}$ moles/liter for near-frozen flow if

$$(-\mathrm{D}T/\mathrm{D}t) \simeq 3 \times 10^{7}\ {}^{\circ}\mathrm{K/sec} \quad .... \ (3.21)$$

Equations 3.18 and 3.21 are typical of the sort of results obtained by application of the flow criteria. To the order of approximation utilized it is only possible to say that for $10^{-7} \leqslant (H)$, moles/liter $\leqslant 3 \times 10^{-4}$ the flow process is neither near-frozen flow nor near-equilibrium flow. The present discussion needs to be supplemented by a proof that the statement $T - T' \leqslant 20°$ K is consistent with Eq. 3.7 and that the assumption $(T_c - T')/(T_c - T) \leqslant 10^{-2}$ is not at variance with Eq. 3.11. These necessary convergence proofs are presented in Sec. 3.5. The analysis presented here can be repeated, without difficulty, for different de Laval nozzles, i.e., for different values of $(-\mathrm{D}T/\mathrm{D}t)$. Summary statements concerning the interplay between chemical reaction rates and rates of cooling are contained in Sec. 3.4.

(*B*) *Reaction between two nitric oxide molecules*

For the reaction

$$2NO \rightarrow N_2 + O_2 \quad .... \ (3.22)$$

it is found from Eq. 3.9 and 3.10 that

$$T' - T \simeq (-\mathrm{D}T/\mathrm{D}t)\left[k_f\{4(NO) + [(N_2) + (O_2)][(NO)^2/(N_2)(O_2)]\}\right]^{-1} \quad .... \ (3.23)$$

According to F. Daniels* $k_f \simeq 10^9 R T_c \exp(-70{,}000/RT_c)$(moles/cm^3)$^{-1}$-sec^{-1}. In a nitric acid-aniline motor at 3000°K and 20 atm. the total numbers of moles of N_2, O_2, and NO present at equilibrium are, respectively, 3·75, 0·0655, and 0·0610. The total concentration is $8{\cdot}23 \times 10^{-5}$ moles/cm^3 and the concentration of the separate species becomes $(N_2) = 1{\cdot}54 \times 10^{-6}$ moles/cm^3, $(O_2) = 2{\cdot}69 \times 10^{-7}$ moles/cm^3, $(NO) = 2{\cdot}51 \times 10^{-7}$ moles/cm^3. In order to maximize $T' - T$ in Eq. 3.23 we again maximize the denominator for the flow process. For $(-\mathrm{D}T/\mathrm{D}t) \simeq 3 \times 10^7$ °K/sec, Eq. 3.23 leads to the conclusion that

$$T' - T > 20 \times 10^{(30,395/RT)-2} \quad .... \ (3.24)$$

i.e., for $T \leqslant 3000°$ K the flow process does not even approximate near-equilibrium flow. The near-equilibrium flow criterion is not capable of yielding a more definitive answer.

* Unpublished measurements obtained in connection with the Wisconsin process for nitrogen fixation. See also reference 6.

For the reaction described by Eq. 3.22 the near-frozen flow criterion given in Eq. 3.14b becomes

$$(T_c - T')/(T_c - T) \leqslant [1 - K_Y(T_c)/K_Y(T)](-\mathrm{D}T/\mathrm{D}t)^{-1}(-RT_c^2/\Delta H_c) \times k_f\{4(\mathrm{NO}) + [(\mathrm{N_2}) + (\mathrm{O_2})][(\mathrm{NO})^2/(\mathrm{N_2})(\mathrm{O_2})]\} \quad \text{....} \quad (3.25)$$

where $-\Delta H_c = 43{,}100$ cals and $(\mathrm{NO})^2/(\mathrm{N_2})(\mathrm{O_2}) \leqslant 66$. Introduction of appropriate numerical values shows that

$$(T_c - T')/(T_c - T) \leqslant 2 \times 10^{-2}[1 - K_Y(T_c)/K_Y(T)] \quad \text{....} \quad (3.26)$$

for $(-\mathrm{D}T/\mathrm{D}t) \simeq 3 \times 10^7$ °K/sec with $K_Y(T_c) \leqslant K_Y(T)$. Hence near-frozen flow with respect to the reaction given in Eq. 3.22 should occur in the nitric acid–aniline motor. This conclusion is in accord with the numerical calculations presented in another publication.[2b]

Repetition of the use of the near-frozen flow calculations for pure NO leads to the conclusion that $(T_c - T')/(T_c - T) \leqslant 22 \times 10^7/(-\mathrm{D}T/\mathrm{D}t)$, i.e., near-frozen flow for pure NO expanding adiabatically from 3000°K cannot occur unless very small nozzles are used to increase the rate of cooling $(-\mathrm{D}T/\mathrm{D}t)$, above the value 3×10^7 °K/sec, which applies to conventional 1000 psia thrust chambers.

(*C*) *The hydrogen–fluorine propellant system*[4]

Representative temperature lags, obtained by use of near-equilibrium flow criteria, for the separate reaction steps in a 1000 psia thrust hydrogen–fluorine rocket motor are the following:

$$\mathrm{H} + \mathrm{H} + X' \rightarrow \mathrm{H_2} + X', \quad T' - T < 25°\mathrm{K}$$
$$\mathrm{F} + \mathrm{F} + X' \rightarrow \mathrm{F_2} + X', \quad T' - T < 25°\mathrm{K}$$
$$\mathrm{H} + \mathrm{F} + X' \rightarrow \mathrm{HF} + X', \quad T' - T \sim 125°\mathrm{K}$$
$$\mathrm{H} + \mathrm{F_2} \rightarrow \mathrm{HF} + \mathrm{F}, \quad T' - T < 6°\mathrm{K}$$
$$\mathrm{H_2} + \mathrm{F_2} \rightarrow 2\mathrm{HF}, \quad T' - T < 6°\mathrm{K}$$

Reference to the results summarized above shows that near-equilibrium flow obtains for all of the separate reaction steps except for the three-body collision leading to the production of HF. In order to deduce a conclusion regarding the gas mixture as a whole, it is evidently necessary to extend the flow criteria to complex chemical reactions. Details concerning a method of approach have been described elsewhere.[7] For most practical purposes it is advantageous to apply the following general rule: near-equilibrium flow will obtain for an interdependent system of chemical reactions if some of the possible reactions occur with sufficient speed to maintain nearly complete thermodynamic equilibrium, and these fast reactions are sufficient in number to allow all of the necessary atomic and molecular concentration changes. For the reaction under discussion the conversion

$$\mathrm{H} + \mathrm{F} + X' \rightarrow \mathrm{HF} + X'$$

can evidently be replaced by the pair of rapid processes

$$H + F_2 \rightarrow HF + F$$
$$F + F + X' \rightarrow F_2 + X'$$

Hence it may be inferred that near-equilibrium flow is maintained for the gas mixture as a whole and the hydrogen–fluorine rocket motor should yield a specific impulse (in 1000 psia or larger thrust motors) approximating equilibrium-flow performance.

3.4. Effect of Nozzle Dimensions on the Occurrence of Chemical Reactions during Adiabatic Flow

Theoretical performance evaluation of propellants in rocket engines is customarily carried out either for chemically-frozen or for equilibrium flow through the nozzle.[8] The equilibrium performance for flow with lags in internal energy has been discussed in general terms[1] and quantitative calculations of performance with and without vibrational equilibrium have been described.[9] In each instance, a realistic estimate of performance requires kinetic studies concerning the interplay between reaction rates and cooling rates. This study is closely related to the motor dimensions.

It is well known that heat losses and deviations from the one-dimensional flow approximation become progressively less important as the motor size is increased. On the other hand, it is not generally appreciated that the theoretical performance, neglecting heat losses, tends to increase with the motor dimensions and that the quantitative dependence on motor size of the extent of chemical reactions during nozzle flow can be approximated by judicious use of the flow criteria.

The general flow criteria (see Eq. 3.9 and 3.14) relate temperature lags to the temperature

$$(-\mathrm{D}T/\mathrm{D}t)(z)$$

where z is a property only of the propellant system, and the coefficient $-(\mathrm{D}T/\mathrm{D}t)$ depends primarily on the nozzle design. The term $-(\mathrm{D}T/\mathrm{D}t)$ is relative insensitive to gas composition, on which it depends only through the quantity γ, viz., the average ratio during flow of heat capacity at constant pressure to heat capacity at constant volume. For adiabatic flow without composition change it is readily shown that[2b]

$$\mathrm{D}T/\mathrm{D}t = (r_e/r)(2\tan\delta/r_e)(2C_pT_c^3/\overline{W})^{(1/2)} \times [(1/2)[1-(T/T_c)]^{-(3/2)} - T_c\{(\gamma-1)T[1-(T/T_c)]^{(1/2)}\}^{-1}]^{-1} \quad \text{.... (3.27)}$$

Here r is the radius of an arbitrary cross section of the nozzle; r_e is the exit radius; δ is the half-angle of the converging cones forming the nozzle*; C_p is the molar heat capacity; $\overline{W}$ represents, as usual, the average molecular weight of the gas mixture. Equation 3.27 can be applied to equilibrium flow by redefining γ to include enthalpy changes associated with chemical reactions.[2] The exact form of Eq. 3.27 depends on the nozzle contour chosen for study and the equation fails to apply in the limit as the nozzle-entrance section is approached. In other words, Eq. 3.27 is not suitable for a determination of the temperature during near-frozen flow when departures from thermodynamic equilibrium first become important. This problem will be treated in Sec. 3.6 in order to illustrate the method for approximating cooling rates in nozzles during one-dimensional adiabatic flow.

The problem of the interrelation between chemical reaction rates and cooling rates can be expressed in general terms as follows. For all chemical reactions near-frozen flow obtains in sufficiently small nozzles. For each propellant system there is a minimum nozzle size which will permit a transition from near-frozen to near-equilibrium flow. Whether or not this critical nozzle size is of reasonable dimensions, and will permit practical utilization of the increase in performance associated with near-equilibrium flow, depends on the rates of the chemical reactions which are characteristic for each propellant system. If the rate processes are understood completely, the problem can be solved exactly, at least in principle. Although specific reaction rate constants are generally not available, useful approximate estimates of the interrelation between nozzle dimensions and chemical reaction rates can be obtained frequently by utilizing the flow criteria and taking advantage of the fact that for conventional nozzle sizes *many chemical reactions are either so rapid as to assure near-equilibrium flow or else so slow as to favor near-frozen flow.*

3.5. Convergence Requirements for the Flow Criteria

A necessary and sufficient condition for the applicability of the flow criteria is rapid convergence of the appropriate Taylor series expansions which were used to define $T' - T$ and $T_c - T'$. The relative magnitudes of the various terms which have been neglected can be ascertained without difficulty. The analysis will be illustrated by studying convergence of the defining relations for near-equilibrium and near-frozen flow for chemical reactions in which the total number of moles of reactants and products is the same.†

* The throat section was rounded off with a radius of curvature equal to the throat diameter. Where the nozzle contour is circular, δ equals the angle between a line through the throat and the radius vector to the nozzle contour (compare reference 2*b*).

† The terms containing Δn, i.e., the change in the number of moles for the stoichiometric reaction, are generally negligibly small. They can be included without difficulty.

The infinite series, of which only the first two terms were used in Eq. 3.7, is

$$K_Y(T')/K_Y(T) = 1 + \sum_{=1}^{\infty} (n!K_Y)^{-1}(\mathrm{d}^n K_Y/\mathrm{d}T^n)(T' - T)^n \quad \text{.... (3.28)}$$

The successive terms appearing in the summation of Eq. 3.28 can be expressed readily in terms of $\mathrm{dln}K_Y/\mathrm{d}T$ and of its derivatives. Thus

$$(K_Y)^{-1}(\mathrm{d}^2K_Y/\mathrm{d}T^2)_T = (\mathrm{dln}K_Y/\mathrm{d}T)^2{}_T + (\mathrm{d}^2\mathrm{ln}K_Y/\mathrm{d}T^2)$$

$$(K_Y)^{-1}(\mathrm{d}^3K_Y/\mathrm{d}T^3)_T = \mathrm{d}[(K_Y)^{-1}(\mathrm{d}^2K_Y/\mathrm{d}T^2)_T]/\mathrm{d}T + (\mathrm{dln}K_Y/\mathrm{d}T)_T(K_Y)^{-1}(\mathrm{d}^2K_Y/\mathrm{d}T^2)_T$$

etc. But, for $\Delta n = 0$,

$$(\mathrm{dln}K_Y/\mathrm{d}T) = (\mathrm{dln}K_p/\mathrm{d}T)$$

or

$$(\mathrm{dln}K_Y/\mathrm{d}T) = \Delta H/RT^2$$

Thus

$$(K_Y)^{-1}(\mathrm{d}^2K_Y/\mathrm{d}T^2)_T = (\Delta H/RT^2)^2 - 2(\Delta H/RT^3)$$

$$(K_Y)^{-1}(\mathrm{d}^3K_Y/\mathrm{d}T^3)_T = (\Delta H/RT^2)^3 - 6(\Delta H^2/R^2T^5) + 6\Delta H/RT^4$$

etc. The quantity $\Delta H/RT$ is usually large compared to unity. Successive terms in Eq. 3.28 differ roughly by the factor $(n^-)^1(\Delta H/RT^2) \times (T' - T)$ and the condition for rapid convergence becomes simply

$$(\Delta H/RT^2)(T' - T) \ll 1 \quad \text{.... (3.29)}$$

Thus, if $\Delta H = 50{,}000$ cals, $T = 2000°\mathrm{K}$, and $T' - T = 20°\mathrm{K}$, the series given in Eq. 3.28 becomes

$$K_Y(T')/K_Y(T) = 1 + (1/8) + (1/2)[(1/8)^2 - (1/400)] + (1/3!)[(1/8)^3(1 - 0{\cdot}240 + 0{\cdot}0384)] + \cdots \quad \text{.... (3.30)}$$

The foregoing illustrative calculation demonstrates the rapidity of convergence of the Taylor series expansion and shows, for example, that the use of the near-equilibrium flow relation introduces an error in $K_Y(T')/K_Y(T)$ of less than 7 per cent if $(\Delta H/RT^2)(T' - T) \leqslant 1/8$. Thus we may adopt this inequality as the criterion which must be satisfied in order to validate the use of near-equilibrium flow relations.

Convergence criteria for near-frozen flow can be developed by proceeding as for near-equilibrium flow. In general, the relation

$$(\Delta H/RT_c^2)(T_c - T') \leqslant 1/8 \quad \text{.... (3.31)}$$

will be a sufficient condition to assure the validity of using the appropriate kinetic criterion for screening slow chemical reactions. If $T' - T$ or $T_c - T'$ are estimated explicitly, it is usually desirable to justify the use of the respective flow criterion by a subsequent examination for rapid convergence of the appropriate Taylor series expansion.

3.6. Rate of Change of Temperature with Time in the Vicinity of the Chamber-Exit Position

For chemical kinetics studies we require only approximate values for the coefficient $-\mathrm{D}T/\mathrm{D}t$. Hence we shall use the customary one-dimensional approximation for nozzle flow analysis.

It follows from the continuity equation that

$$\rho A u = \rho_c A_c u_c = \rho_t A_t u_t = \text{constant} \qquad \text{.... (3.32)}$$

where ρ is the density, A represents the cross-sectional area, and u denotes a linear flow velocity. The subscripts c and t denote conditions at the chamber-exit position and at the nozzle throat, respectively. It is well known that the linear flow velocity at the nozzle throat for one-dimensional flow is sonic. Hence

$$u_t = (\gamma p_t/\rho_t)^{(1/2)} \qquad \text{.... (3.33)}$$

where p represents the pressure and γ is the ratio of the specific heat at constant pressure to the specific heat at constant volume. In view of the use of one-dimensional flow analysis it is hardly justified to consider the (usually rather small) temperature dependence of γ. For simplicity we shall therefore assume that γ and C_p, the heat capacity at constant pressure per mole of gas mixture, are constants for the system under discussion. Finally we shall assume the validity of the ideal gas law, i.e.,

$$p = \rho R T/\overline{W} \qquad \text{.... (3.34)}$$

where R represents the molar gas constant. The expansion through the nozzle will be assumed to be adiabatic whence it follows that

$$(\rho_t/\rho_c) = [2/(\gamma+1)]^{(\gamma-1)^{-1}} \qquad \text{.... (3.35)}$$

Introducing Eq. 3.33 to 3.35 into Eq. 3.32 it is found that

$$u_c = (A_t/A_c)[2/(\gamma+1)]^{(\gamma-1)^{-1}}(\gamma R T_t/\overline{W})^{(1/2)} \qquad \text{.... (3.36)}$$

For representative rocket motors we have $A_c/A_t = 4$, $\gamma = 1{\cdot}25$, $T_t = 2500°\mathrm{K}$ and $\overline{W} = 20$ g/mole. Hence it follows that

$$u_c \simeq 1{\cdot}8 \times 10^4 \text{ cm/sec} \simeq 600 \text{ ft/sec} \qquad \text{.... (3.37)}$$

Although the value of u_c listed in Eq. 3.37 will vary from one propellant system to another and is also dependent on the ratio A_c/A_t, we may consider the numerical value given in Eq. 3.37 as a representative order-of-magnitude estimate for liquid-fuel rocket engines.

In order to determine conveniently the temperature-time history during nozzle flow, we consider the chamber to consist of a circular cylinder. The cylinder is joined to the contracting section of the de Laval nozzle by a sphere which is tangent to the cylinder at the chamber exit position and also to the cone (contracting section of the nozzle) whose apex lies to the right of the nozzle throat. A cross-sectional drawing showing the chamber exit section and its junction to the nozzle is shown in *Fig. 3.2.* It should be noted that the exact shape of the exit section will have no significant effect on the results regarding chemical kinetics analysis. The particular form shown in *Fig. 3.2* was chosen because of its mathematical simplicity rather than because of its correspondence to physical reality. If r denotes the

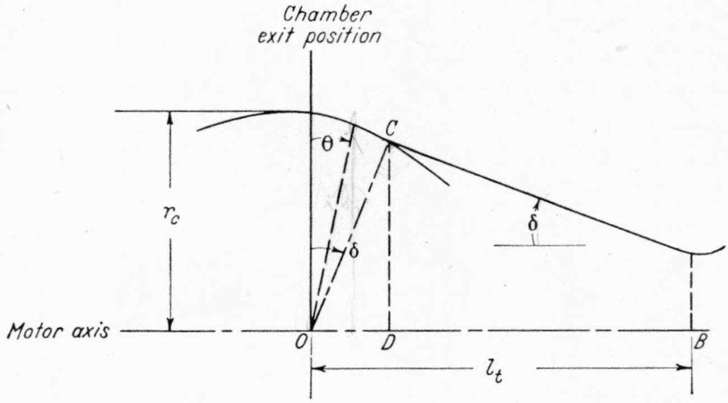

Fig. 3.2. Cross-sectional drawing showing the exit section of a combustion chamber (idealized)

radius of a (circular) cross-section normal to the motor axis, it is evident from *Fig. 3.2* that for $\theta < \delta$

$$r = r_c \cos\theta, \quad dr = -r_c \sin\theta \, d\theta$$

$$x = r_c \sin\theta, \quad dx = r_c \cos\theta \, d\theta$$

Hence

$$dr = -dx \tan\theta, \ (\theta < \delta)$$

where x is the axial distance measured from the center of the circle at O. Also, for the region extending to the right of the plane CD,

$$dr = -dx \tan\delta$$

Thus

$$dr = -dx \tan\theta, \ (\theta \leqslant \delta)$$

or

$$(-dx/dT) = (\tan\theta)^{-1}(dr/dT), \ (\theta \leqslant \delta) \quad .... \ (3.38)$$

Since

$$(-Dt/dT) = (u)^{-1}(-dx/dT) \quad .... \ (3.39)$$

it follows from Eq. 3.38 that

$$(-Dt/dT) = (u \tan\theta)^{-1}(dr/dT), \ (\theta \leqslant \delta) \quad .... \ (3.40)$$

We next proceed to replace the coefficient dr/dT in terms of functions of pressure and temperature alone by utilizing the same type of analysis which has been employed for evaluating the coefficient $-\mathrm{D}t/\mathrm{d}T$ in the vicinity of the nozzle throat.[2] Thus, utilizing Eq. 3.32 and 3.34 and the adiabatic law in the form

$$\mathrm{d}\ln p/\mathrm{d}T = \gamma/T(\gamma-1)$$

it is readily shown that

$$\mathrm{d}r/\mathrm{d}T = (r/2)\{(-\mathrm{d}\ln u/\mathrm{d}T) - [T(\gamma-1)]^{-1}\} \quad .... \ (3.41)$$

For the present case, with the molar heat capacity C_p and the molecular weight $\overline{W}$ independent of temperature, the expression for the conservation of energy becomes

$$\overline{W}u\mathrm{d}u = -C_p\mathrm{d}T \quad .... \ (3.42)$$

or

$$-\mathrm{d}\ln u/\mathrm{d}T = C_p/\overline{W}u^2 \quad .... \ (3.43)$$

and

$$u = \{u_c^2 + [2C_p(T_c - T)/\overline{W}]\}^{(1/2)} \quad .... \ (3.44)$$

Combining Eq. 3.41 with Eq. 3.43 and introducing the resulting expression into Eq. 3.40 leads to the conclusion that

$$-\mathrm{D}t/\mathrm{D}T = (r/2u \tan\theta)\{(C_p/\overline{W}u^2) - [T(\gamma-1)]^{-1}\}, \ (\theta \leqslant \delta) \quad .... \ (3.45)$$

Since we are interested in obtaining a relation between the coefficient $-\mathrm{D}T/\mathrm{D}t$ and the temperature T in terms of the nozzle design parameters and of the physico-chemical properties which are characteristic of the propellants used, we proceed by obtaining a relation between r and T. If C_p is independent of T, then Eq. 3.42 can be integrated with the result

$$\overline{W}u^2 = 2C_p(T_c - T) + \overline{W}u_c^2 \quad .... \ (3.46)$$

Replacing $\overline{W}u^2$ in Eq. 3.43 by the use of Eq. 3.46 leads to the relation

$$-\mathrm{d}\ln u = -\mathrm{d}\ln[2C_p(T_c - T) + \overline{W}u_c^2]^{(1/2)} \quad .... \ (3.47)$$

By the use of Eq. 3.41 and 3.47 we obtain, after integration between T_c and T, corresponding to the radii r_c and r, respectively, the desired result,* viz.,

$$(r/r_c)^2 = (T_c/T)^{(\gamma-1)^{-1}}\{\overline{W}u_c^2/[2C_p(T_c - T) + \overline{W}u_c^2]\}^{(1/2)} \quad .... \ (3.48)$$

In order to obtain a relation between θ and T (for $\theta < \delta$) it is merely necessary to replace r by $r_c \cos\theta$ in Eq. 3.48, i.e.,

$$\cos^2\theta = (T_c/T)^{(\gamma-1)^{-1}}\{\overline{W}u_c^2/[2C_p(T_c - T) + \overline{W}u_c^2]\}^{(1/2)}, \ (\theta < \delta) \quad .... \ (3.49)$$

It is interesting to note that the relation between θ and T is independent of the design parameter r_c.

* For the analysis of nozzle flow processes in which the assumption $u_c = 0$ is made, it has been customary to determine the ratio r/r_c rather than r_c/r, which, however, is a more convenient variable for the problem at hand.

Equations 3.48 and 3.49 have been used to determine the relation between $r/r_c = \cos\,\theta$ and T for $u_c = 1{\cdot}8 \times 10^4$ cm/sec, $C_p = 10$ cals/(mole of gas mixture), $\overline{W} = 20$ g/mole, $\gamma = 1{\cdot}25$ and $T_c = 3000°$K. The quantities

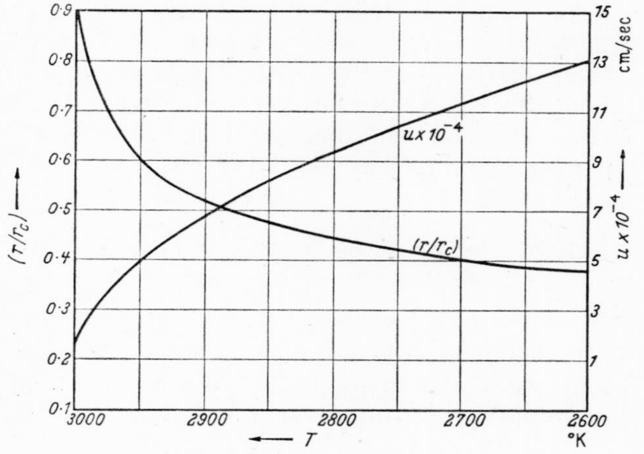

T, °K

Fig. 3.3. Dependence of (r/r_c) *and of* u *on* T *in the contracting section of the nozzle*

$r/r_c = \cos\,\theta$ and the linear flow velocity u are plotted in *Fig. 3.3* as a function of T. Next the coefficient $-\mathrm{D}t/\mathrm{D}T$ has been computed from Eq. 3.45 in the vicinity of the nozzle entrance position for $r_c = 5$ cm. The results of these calculations are plotted in *Fig. 3.4*. It can be seen

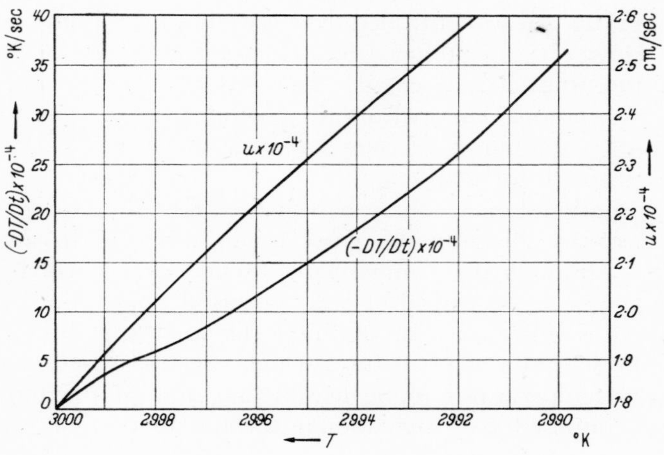

T, °*K*.

Fig. 3.4. Dependence of $(-\mathrm{d}T/\mathrm{d}t)$ *and of* u *on* T *in the vicinity of the chamber-exit position*

from Eq. 3.49 that for $\theta < \delta$ the coefficient $(-Dt/DT)$ is directly proportional to r_c since θ is independent of r_c.*

In so far as application to analysis of chemical reactions during nozzle flow is concerned, the preceding results are of interest since they show a very rapid increase of the coefficient $-DT/Dt$ in the vicinity of the nozzle entrance section [see *Fig. 3.4*]. By the time the gases have been cooled about 100°K, the coefficient $(-DT/Dt)$ has a value of about 3×10^7 °K/sec for representative 1000 psia thrust motors. Hence, even for the analysis of near-frozen flow, it is not unreasonable to use large values for $(-DT/Dt)$.

3.7. Use of the de Laval Nozzle in Processes for the Production of Chemicals

The methods of analysis described in the preceding sections can be inverted, without difficulty, to use measurements of composition profiles (or, in some cases, of pressure profiles) during flow through nozzles for the determination of fast reaction rates. The experimental techniques required for studies of this type are not simple and, as yet, few, if any, significant experimental results have been described in the literature.

The high rates of change of temperature with time during expansion through a de Laval nozzle can be utilized, in principle, to 'freeze' chemical compositions at chamber conditions. For example, nitric oxide produced under equilibrium conditions in the combustion chamber, if natural gas is burnt in excess air, can be retained if sufficiently high cooling rates are available. This principle is used in both the arc process and in the Wisconsin process for nitrogen fixation.

Cooling rates can be controlled over wide limits by using a de Laval nozzle. However, since the nozzle is essentially a device for converting thermal into translational energy, methods must be devised for abstracting translational energy from the flowing gases in order to prevent reheating to stagnation conditions and reversal of the cooling process after flow through the nozzle.

The translational energy may be removed advantageously from the flowing gases by allowing the gases to do work, as in an impulse turbine.[10] Although no commercially useful cycles involving nozzle cooling have been developed as yet, successful application to process development is only a question of time. The principal difficulty seems to lie in the selection of procedures which can be carried out at sufficiently low temperatures to be feasible in view of the temperature limitations imposed by conventional turbine blades. Probably the

* It is, of course, obvious that the present analysis treats only the converging part of the nozzle. This part of the nozzle is the only portion which is of interest for frozen-flow calculations. A discussion of the variation of $-Dt/DT$ with T in the vicinity of the nozzle throat and in the expanding section of the nozzle has been given in references 2*a* and 2*b*.

greatest promise lies in the development of non-equilibrium chemical processes in which valuable unstable reaction intermediates are manufactured in low-temperature processes. For example, it is possible that hydrazine can be produced in significant quantities by partial burning of ammonia, followed by judicious cooling in a de Laval nozzle, with removal of translational energy from the expanded gases through a suitably chosen turbine cycle. Similarly, the ultimate success of producing reaction intermediates by partial burning of hydrocarbons can hardly be assessed at the present time. A great deal of exploratory experimentation will have to be done; quantitative theoretical studies are ruled out by the absence of relevant kinetics data.

Nozzle flow processes for the production of chemicals can be made continuous without difficulty. Thus a tremendous rate of production of chemicals should be feasible for relatively small nozzles.

REFERENCES

[1] PENNER, S. S., *J. chem. Phys.* 19 (1951) 877; 20 (1952) 341

[2] (*a*) PENNER, S. S., and ALTMAN, D., *J. Franklin Inst.* 245 (1948) 421; (*b*) ALTMAN, D., and PENNER, S. S., *J. chem. Phys.* 17 (1949) 56

[3] PENNER, S. S., *J. Amer. chem. Soc.* 71 (1949) 788

[4] —, *J. Franklin Inst.* 249 (1950) 441

[5] AMDUR, I., *J. Amer. chem. Soc.* 60 (1935) 2347

[6] WISE, H., and FRECH, M., *J. chem. Phys.* 20 (1952) 22

[7] PENNER, S. S., *J. chem. Phys.* 17 (1949) 841

[8] —, *Amer. J. Phys.* 20 (1952) 26

[9] —, *J. appl. Phys.* 20 (1949) 445; SCHROEDER, J. H., *J. Amer. Rocket Soc.* 23 (1953) 25

[10] MACLEOD, G., M.E. Thesis, California Inst. Technol., June 1953; abstr. *J. Amer. Rocket Soc.* 24 (1954) 111

CHAPTER 4

HETEROGENEOUS CHEMICAL REACTIONS

THE chemist usually defines heterogeneous chemical reactions as processes in which phenomena occurring at the phase boundaries (e.g., at the gas–liquid, gas–solid, or liquid–solid interfaces) play an important role. We shall enlarge on this definition and refer to all chemical reactions involving two- or multi-phase systems as heterogeneous chemical reactions, even though (rate-controlling) chemical changes may not actually occur at the phase boundary.

In this chapter we present a brief summary of some of the important properties of gas reactions on solid surfaces (Sec. 4.1) and of the Semenoff theory of explosions together with qualitative descriptions of explosion limits in stationary chain reactions (Sec. 4.2). Finally, the heterogeneous burning of single droplets of liquid in an oxidizing atmosphere is treated according to a first approximation in which the chemical reaction rates are not rate-controlling (Sec. 4.3).

4.1. Reactions on Solid Surfaces

A number of gas reactions on solid surfaces can be understood in terms of the theory of adsorption proposed by LANGMUIR[1], which has undergone considerable evolution, particularly in connection with studies on catalysis.[2] If a unimolecular adsorbed layer of gas is formed on a solid, then the fraction of the surface covered at equilibrium, f, is determined by the condition that the rate of adsorption of molecules on the surface, $(1-f)\alpha\eta$, equals the rate of desorption of molecules from the surface (δf), i.e.,

$$f = \frac{\alpha\eta}{\alpha\eta + \delta} \qquad \text{.... (4.1)}$$

Here $1-f$ equals the fraction of surface not covered by a unimolecular layer; α represents the fraction of molecules, striking bare surface, which is adsorbed; η is the number of molecules striking unit area of surface per second; δ equals the probability that an adsorbed molecule will become desorbed from the surface in unit time. After condensing on the solid surface, the chemical compounds may decompose. If the rate of chemical reaction is small compared to the rates of adsorption and of desorption, Eq. 4.1 will still hold in good approximation. Since η is proportional to the pressure, Eq. 4.1 can also be written in the form

$$c' = c_o' \frac{ap}{1+ap} \qquad \text{.... (4.2)}$$

where c' is the actual number of molecules adsorbed per unit area, c_0' is the number of molecules which would be adsorbed if the surface were completely covered, and a is a constant.

At low and moderate temperatures, surfaces often play a vital role in the destruction of chain carriers.[3] Annihilation of chain carriers may occur as the result of direct reaction with the wall or, alternately, as the result of a heterogeneous reaction between several adsorbed gas molecules, with the surface acting as an energy sink. The ability to destroy chains varies greatly with the type of surface; a given surface may be 'poisoned' as a chain destroyer by covering it with a monomolecular layer of inert material. For example, adsorbed water molecules may decrease the probability of destruction of hydrogen atoms on the surface of glass by many orders of magnitude. Poisoning of surfaces may also be accomplished by reaction products, in which case a strongly self-inhibited chemical reaction will be observed.

For bimolecular chemical reactions involving A and B, the analytical description of surface effects depends upon the extent of surface adsorption for the two reacting gases and for the reaction products. If the reaction products are not adsorbed appreciably and chemical reaction between adsorbed molecules occurs rapidly, then we may set the fraction of uncovered surface equal to unity, in first approximation. In this case we find at equilibrium that

$$\alpha_A \eta_A = \delta_A f_A, \quad \alpha_B \eta_B = \delta_B f_B \qquad .... \quad (4.3)$$

For a bimolecular surface reaction between adsorbed molecules according to the process

$$A + B \rightarrow \text{reaction products}$$

it follows that

$$-\mathrm{d}(A)/\mathrm{d}t = -\mathrm{d}(B)/\mathrm{d}t = k_s' f_A f_B = k_s p_A p_B \qquad .... \quad (4.4)$$

where k_s' and k_s are constants.

The chain-destroying properties of surfaces must be included in the phenomenological description of heterogeneous reaction rates. Needless to say, both stationary and flow problems are materially simplified if it can be demonstrated that surface reactions are unimportant. In stationary and isothermal systems, the proof that surface reactions can be neglected may be provided by experiments which show that the observed overall specific reaction rate constant is independent of the type of surface (the surface is varied in different experiments by using different reaction vessels) or, more conveniently, is independent of the surface to gas volume ratio (this ratio can be varied over very wide limits by packing the reaction vessel with finely divided glass, quartz, or metal beads). The fact that surface effects are unimportant in flow systems can be demonstrated similarly for some systems. For example, for relatively wide limits of burner and tube design, detonation and deflagration velocities in many gas mixtures have been found to be independent of the surface; in these cases the observed reaction velocities must therefore be those of a homogeneous chemical reaction.

4.2. THE SEMENOFF THEORY OF EXPLOSION LIMITS[4–6]

Following SEMENOFF[4], it is instructive to describe chain reactions by the relation

$$\frac{d(Z)}{dt} = (\dot{Z})_i - \beta(Z)^q + \phi(Z)^{q'} \qquad \text{.... (4.5)}$$

Here (Z) equals the total concentration of chain carriers; $(\dot{Z})_i$ is the rate of production of chain carriers by chain-initiating reactions, which is generally independent of (Z); β and ϕ are referred to as the coefficients of chain breaking and chain branching, respectively. The coefficients β and ϕ are determined, in general, by a series of interdependent chemical reactions.

For $q=q'$ and $\phi \geqslant \beta$, the chain-carrier concentration increases exponentially with time and a branching-chain explosion results. For $q=q'$ and $\phi<\beta$, a steady-state value $(Z)_s$ is reached, which is given by the relation

$$(Z)_s = \left[\frac{(\dot{Z})_i}{\beta - \phi}\right]^{1/q} \qquad \text{.... (4.6)}$$

The condition $\phi = \beta$ is said to define the explosion limit for $q=q'$.

If chain breaking occurs as the result of a reaction involving two molecules of chain carrier, whereas chain branching requires only one molecule of chain carrier, then Eq. 4.5 becomes

$$\frac{d(Z)}{dt} = (\dot{Z})_i - \beta(Z)^2 + \phi(Z) \qquad \text{.... (4.7)}$$

and the steady-state value of (Z) is

$$(Z)_s = (\phi/2\beta)\{1 + \sqrt{1 + [4\beta(\dot{Z})_i/\phi^2]}\} \qquad \text{.... (4.8)}$$

It is evident from Eq. 4.8 that $(Z)_s$ is always finite and, therefore, a branching-chain explosion will not occur. In the initial stages of branching-chain explosions the chain-carrier concentrations are too low to permit significant chain-breaking by simultaneous removal of two chain carriers.

For a gas at rest the general continuity equation for chain carriers can be obtained from Eq. 2.15 which leads to the result

$$\frac{\partial(Z)}{\partial t} = -\nabla.[(Z)\vec{V}_Z] + \gamma_Z \qquad \text{.... (4.9)}$$

for a constant density (i.e., constant pressure and temperature) process, where $\vec{V}_Z$ is the diffusion velocity of the chain carriers, and γ_Z denotes the mole rate of production of chain carrier per unit volume by chemical reaction. In first approximation, the gas mixture may be considered to consist of chain carriers and other molecules, in which case

$$\vec{V}_Z = -D\nabla(Z)/(Z)$$

since $(Z) = \rho Y_Z / W_Z$ with ρ and W_Z constant [see Eq. 2.27]. Hence Eq. 4.9 becomes, for a spherically symmetric system,

$$\frac{\partial(Z)}{\partial t} = D\frac{1}{r^2}\frac{\partial}{\partial r}\left[r^2\frac{\partial(Z)}{\partial r}\right] + \gamma_Z \qquad \text{....} \quad (4.10)$$

The steady-state solution of Eq. 4.10 provides the starting-point for a quantitative discussion of explosion limits in spherical reaction vessels.[6]

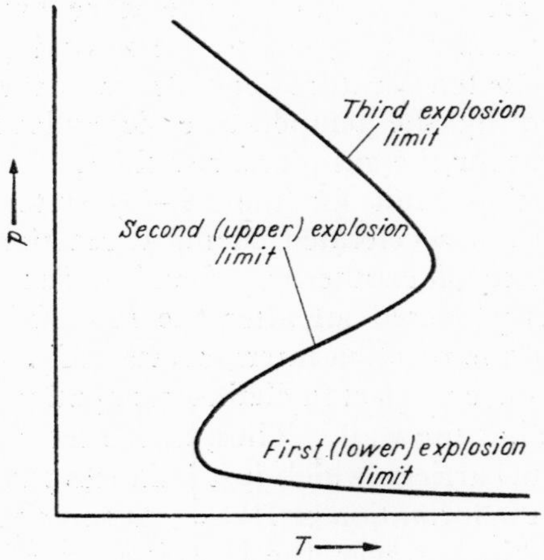

Fig. 4.1. Schematic plot of gas pressure vs. gas temperature for $H_2 - O_2$ mixtures, showing the explosion limits

The existence of explosion limits in closed vessels can be understood very simply from qualitative considerations of competition between chain-breaking and chain-branching reactions on surfaces and in the gas phase. Typical experimental results for hydrogen–oxygen mixtures are shown schematically in *Fig. 4.1* in which the explosion limits are shown as solid lines on a plot of gas pressure versus gas temperature. Chemical reaction without explosion is observed for initial conditions lying to the left and below the explosion limit line; to the right and above the limit line, explosions are observed.

The first or lower explosion limit occurs at roughly the same pressure for a relatively large temperature range. The lower explosion limit is determined by a balance between the removal of chain carriers on the surface and the production of chain carriers by gas-phase reactions. As the pressure is raised, the rate of production of chain carriers by gas phase reactions increases to the point where surface destruction is no longer sufficient to prevent a branched-chain explosion. The lower explosion limit defines the conditions at which chain-branching in the gas phase is just balanced by chain-breaking at the surface.

It has been found experimentally that the second explosion limit is practically independent of vessel dimensions and surface type, and that explosion is inhibited by the addition of foreign gases. It follows, therefore, that the second explosion limit must be determined by gas-phase reactions. The chain-breaking processes in the gas phase (which are unimportant compared to surface chain-breaking at and below the first explosion limit) are generally of the third order, whereas the chain-branching reactions are usually of the second order. Therefore, as the pressure is raised, chain-breaking in the gas phase must ultimately balance chain-branching in the gas phase. When this limiting condition is reached at fixed temperature, explosions no longer occur; the limiting line corresponds to the second (upper) explosion limit of *Fig. 4.1.* The temperature dependence of the upper explosion limit is determined by the temperature dependence of the chain-branching coefficient for the gas-phase reactions.

The third explosion limit for the H_2–O_2 system was originally 'explained' in terms of accelerated chemical reaction rates associated with the heat release of exothermic chemical reactions. However, HINSHELWOOD[7] has proposed an alternate mechanism based on the special properties of the reaction intermediate HO_2. At low pressures HO_2 is assumed to have no part in chain-propagation or chain-branching and is destroyed at the wall. Thus, at the second explosion limit, the removal of chain carriers, which just balances the chain-branching reactions, involves the formation of HO_2. At some pressure above the second explosion limit, however, the HO_2 is assumed to participate in the chain-propagating processes according to the reaction

$$HO_2 + H_2 \rightarrow H_2O + OH$$

Therefore, above a critical pressure, there occurs a rapid increase in the number of radicals. This critical pressure defines the third explosion limit.

Detailed discussions concerning the chemistry of explosion limits in stationary systems for a variety of gas mixtures may be found in the books of SEMENOFF[4], LEWIS and VON ELBE[6], and LAIDLER[8]. Treatments of explosion limits in flow systems can presumably be worked out by an extension of the methods developed for closed reaction vessels. Extensive experimental data on explosion limits in flow systems are not available.

4.3. Burning of Single Drops of Fuel in Oxidizing Atmospheres *

In the preceding sections we have stressed the complications associated with heterogeneous chemical reactions if chemical reaction rates are rate-controlling. For some multiphase systems a successful first approximation to the burning processes can sometimes be worked out on the assumption that observable results are determined by transport phenomena. An interesting example is provided by the burning of single droplets of fuel in an oxidizing atmosphere, which may have some relation to air-fuel combustion in turbojet engines.

(*A*) *Introduction*

In recent years many publications have appeared on the important problem of heterogeneous combustion.[9] Studies on the burning of single fuel droplets in an oxidizing atmosphere have been carried out by Godsave[10–12], Topps[13], and Spalding[14] in England as well as by a group of Japanese investigators.[15] Experimental data on the burning of single drops of fuel have been published by Godsave[11] and Topps[13]. Topps[13] studied the rate of burning of small fuel drops falling through a heated oxidizing atmosphere. Godsave[11] suspended small droplets on a fine quartz fibre and examined the burning droplet and the flame as a function of time. In this way quantitative data were obtained for the rate of burning of the suspended droplet. Godsave[10,12] obtained a successful interpretation of his results on the assumption that the chemical reaction rates do not control the rate of burning. This hypothesis simplifies the analytical treatment considerably.

Following Godsave[10], Spalding[14] and others, we postulate the following mechanism for the combustion processes: oxidizer is delivered from the surrounding atmosphere to the region of active combustion by convection and diffusion; the fuel evaporates and diffuses, without chemical change, to the reaction front, which is assumed to be a spherical shell surrounding the droplet. The location of the reaction front is defined by the condition that the ratio of the mass rate of delivery of fuel to oxidizer corresponds to stoichiometric proportions. It is assumed that the reactants are consumed instantaneously upon reaching the flame front. The problem of determining the rate of burning therefore is reduced to finding the solution of the appropriate transfer problem. Because it is to be expected that the rates of mass and heat transfer will be increased by the effects of convection, a lower limit for the burning rate will be obtained if the analysis is made for a droplet burning in a still atmosphere, by neglecting the convection of hot

* Based, in part, on Goldsmith, M. and Penner, S. S. 'On the Burning of Single Drops of Fuel in an Oxidizing Atmosphere', *Tech. Rep.* No. 2, *Contr.* DA 04-495-Ord-446, Off. Ordnance Res., U.S. Army, *Calif. Inst. Tech.*, November 1953.

gases over the fuel droplet. Although fuel may be injected into the combustion chamber of an engine at a velocity appreciably different from the gas velocity in the chamber, it appears likely that, in some cases, the droplet is slowed down rapidly to the local gas velocity because of aerodynamic drag.

In the following Sec. 4.3*B* a theory for the burning of a droplet in a still atmosphere will be presented. The comparison of theoretical results with experimental studies is carried out in Sec. 4.3*C*. The analysis differs from that of Godsave in that only integrated forms for the energy and continuity equations are used, thereby simplifying the analytical treatment since only first-order differential equations occur. Explicit expressions for the mass rate of fuel flow are derived without introducing such invalid approximations as constant thermal conductivity and specific heat of fuel vapor, constant values for the ratio of specific heat to thermal conductivity, or constant values for the product of density and diffusion coefficient. Furthermore, Godsave's analysis is extended in two important respects by obtaining explicit expressions for (*a*) the temperature of the combustion surface, and (*b*) the radius of the combustion surface.

(*B*) *A simplified model for the burning of single drops of fuel*

The important assumptions upon which the analysis is based are the following:

1. The droplets are spherical.
2. Convection effects may be neglected.
3. The flame front surrounding the drop is represented by a spherical surface concentric with the drop. All reactions take place instantaneously at this surface, at which the delivery rates of fuel to oxidizer are in stoichiometric proportions.
4. Steady-state conditions are assumed for fixed droplet sizes. This restriction greatly facilitates the mathematical treatment. It is reasonable to assume that the solution obtained for a fixed size applies to a drop decreasing in size when it reaches the radius used in the steady-state solution.
5. The effect of heat transfer by radiation is neglected.
6. Mean values will be used, when appropriate, for the physical properties.
7. The temperature of the liquid drop is assumed to be uniform and equal to the boiling temperature. Although this assumption is questionable,[16,17] it does not exert a large effect on the theoretical results.
8. The pressure is assumed to be uniform throughout the system.

A schematic diagram of an evaporating and burning fuel droplet in an oxidizing atmosphere is shown in *Fig. 4.2*. The radius of the liquid drop is r_l and its temperature is the normal boiling point T_l. The radial distance of the combustion surface from the center of the liquid droplet is r_c and its temperature is T_c. The oxygen–inert gas

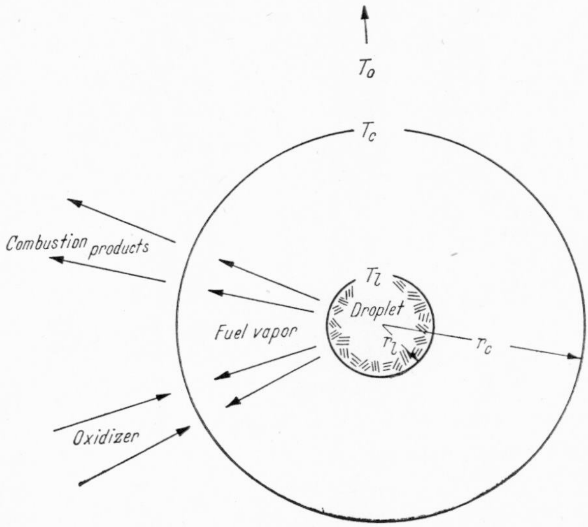

Fig. 4.2. Schematic diagram of burning fuel drop

mixture at a large distance from the combustion surface is at the temperature T_o. In order to clarify further the physical picture, we show in *Fig. 4.3a* a plot of the temperature (T) as a function of the

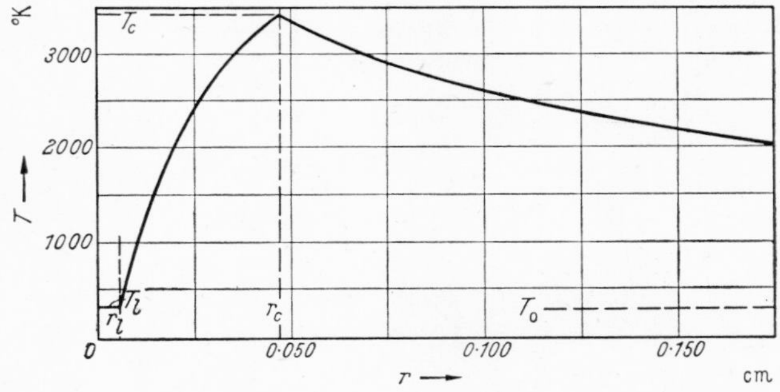

Fig. 4.3a. Temperature (T) as a function of distance from center of drop (r) for 0·010 *cm diameter benzene droplet burning in air at atmospheric pressure*

radial distance (r) from the center of the drop and, in *Fig. 4.3b* to *4.3d*, diagrams of the weight fractions of fuel (Y_F), oxidizer (Y_O), and inert gas (Y_I) as a function of r. The data shown in *Fig. 4.3a* to *4.3d* correspond to the burning of a droplet of benzene in air for $r_l = 0{\cdot}005$ cm and $T_o = 300°K$ (compare Sec. 4.3*C*). The profile for the weight fraction of inert gas has been drawn on the assumption that the physical properties of combustion products and inert gas (in the oxidizer–inert gas mixture) are alike. If this assumption is not made, ternary gas

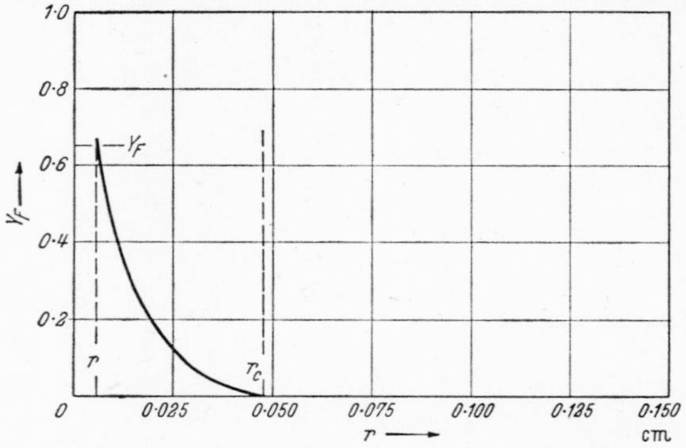

Fig. 4.3b. *Weight fraction of fuel vapor* (Y_F) *as function of distance from center of drop* (r) *for* 0·010 *cm diameter benzene droplet burning in air at atmospheric pressure*

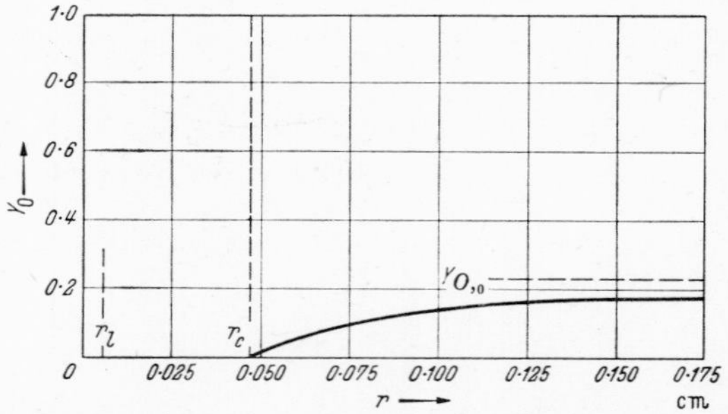

Fig. 4.3c. *Weight fraction of oxygen* (Y_O) *as function of distance from center of drop* (r) *for* 0·010 *cm diameter benzene droplet burning in air at atmospheric pressure*

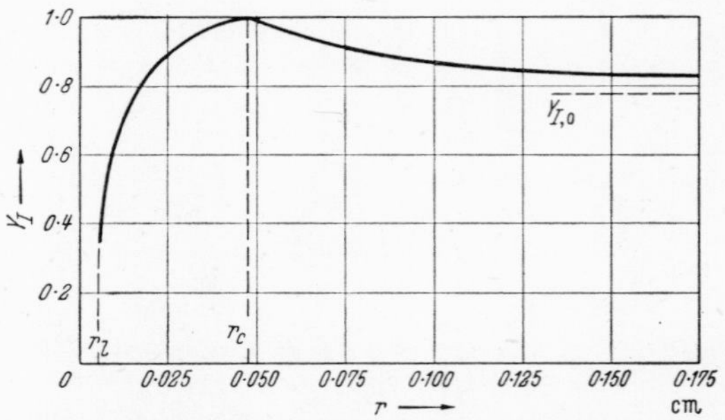

Fig. 4.3d. *Weight fraction of inert gas* (Y_I) *as function of distance from center of drop* (r) *for* 0·010 *cm diameter benzene droplet burning in air at atmospheric pressure*

mixtures must be treated both for $r<r_c$ and for $r>r_c$. This refinement can be introduced without difficulty but does not appear to be warranted in view of the crudeness of the physical model.

Let $\dot{m}_F$ represent the steady-state mass rate of fuel consumption, which is the desired eigenvalue of our boundary-value problem; t is the time; ρ, c_p, and λ represent, respectively, the density, specific heat at constant pressure, and thermal conductivity; Δl equals the specific latent heat of evaporation of the fuel.

For a constant-pressure flow process,* the first law of thermodynamics leads to the relation

$$\mathrm{d}h/\mathrm{d}t = \mathrm{d}q/\mathrm{d}t$$

where $\mathrm{d}h/\mathrm{d}t$ is the rate of enthalpy increase of the gases passing through a fixed volume to which the total rate of energy transfer is $\mathrm{d}q/\mathrm{d}t$. For a spherical shell bounded by the radii r_i and r_f, the energy equation takes the following simple form:

$$(\mathrm{d}h/\mathrm{d}t)_f - (\mathrm{d}h/\mathrm{d}t)_i = -\{[4\pi r^2\lambda(\mathrm{d}T/\mathrm{d}r)]_i - [4\pi r^2\lambda(\mathrm{d}T/\mathrm{d}r)]_f\} \quad .... \; (4.11)$$

Here the subscripts i and f identify, respectively, the surfaces at r_i and r_f.

The general continuity equation for species K can be written in the form

$$\dot{m}_K = 4\pi r^2 \rho Y_K[(\dot{m}_F/4\pi r^2\rho) - (\mathrm{D}_K/Y_K)(\mathrm{d}Y_K/\mathrm{d}r)] \quad .... \; (4.12)$$

where $\dot{m}_K$ is the rate of mass transport of species K, ρ is the density of the gas mixture, Y_K equals the weight fraction of species K, and D_K is the appropriate diffusion coefficient for species K. Equation 4.12 states that the total mass transport of species K is equal to the sum of the mass transport of species K associated with the movement of the average fluid, $Y_K\dot{m}_F$, and with mass transfer by diffusion, $-4\pi r^2\rho\mathrm{D}_K(\mathrm{d}Y_K/\mathrm{d}r)$.

(*a*) *Derivation of Godsave's equation for* $\dot{m}_F$[10]—We apply the expression for conservation of energy, which is given in Eq. 4.11, to the spherical shell between r_l and r for $r<r_c$. The rate of enthalpy transport† at r_l is

$$\dot{m}_F(h_F)_{T_l}$$

and at r

$$\dot{m}_F(h_F)_T$$

The rate of energy transport by thermal conduction at r_l is

$$-[4\pi r^2\lambda(\mathrm{d}T/\mathrm{d}r)]_{r_l} = -\dot{m}_F\Delta l$$

and the rate of energy transport at r into the spherical shell between r_l and r is

$$4\pi r^2\lambda(\mathrm{d}T/\mathrm{d}r)$$

Hence Eq. 4.11 becomes

$$\dot{m}_F[(h_F)_T - (h_F)_{T_l}] = -\dot{m}_F\Delta l + 4\pi r^2\lambda(\mathrm{d}T/\mathrm{d}r)$$

or

$$4\pi r^2(\mathrm{d}T/\mathrm{d}r) = (\dot{m}_F/\lambda)[\Delta l + \int_{T_l}^{T}(c_p)_F\mathrm{d}T] \quad .... \; (4.13)$$

* In the formulation of the problem no explicit use is made of the momentum equation. It is easily shown that the condition for conservation of momentum reduces to the statement that the pressure is practically constant, which is assumed to be the case in the analysis.

† For steady burning the net mass flow out from the droplet for all values of $r \geqslant r_l$ is $\dot{m}_F$.

where the subscript $_F$ to the specific heat identifies the fuel vapor. If it is assumed that $\lambda=\lambda_1$ is independent of temperature and also that $(c_p)_F=(c_p)_{F1}$ is constant, then Eq. 4.13 becomes

$$4\pi r^2(\mathrm{d}T/\mathrm{d}r)=[\dot{m}_F(c_p)_{F1}/\lambda_1]\{[\Delta l/(c_p)_{F1}]+(T-T_l)\}$$

Integration of the preceding expression between the limits $r=r_l$ at $T=T_l$ and $r=r_c$ at $T=T_c$ leads directly to Godsave's equation for $\dot{m}_F$, viz.,

$$\dot{m}_F=\frac{4\pi\lambda_1}{(c_p)_{F1}}\frac{\ln\{1+[(c_p)_{F1}(T_c-T_l)/\Delta l]\}}{(1/r_l)-(1/r_c)} \quad \text{.... (4.14)}$$

Reference to Eq. 4.14 shows that for $r_c \gg r_l$, or for constant values of r_l/r_c, $\dot{m}_F$ is a linear function of the droplet radius. Furthermore, since T_c is generally large compared to T_l, it follows that $\dot{m}_F$ is not a sensitive function of T_l.

It should be noted that Eq. 4.14 was derived without making any special assumptions about the location of the reaction front. For this reason the expression for $\dot{m}_F$ contains two unknown parameters, viz., T_c and r_c. Godsave measured* r_c and showed that for reasonable, assumed, values of T_c an acceptable correlation for the measured values of $\dot{m}_F$ was provided by Eq. 4.14.

(*b*) *An expression for $\dot{m}_F$ if λ and $(c_p)_F$ are linear functions of the temperature*—A refinement of Godsave's equation can be obtained without difficulty by deleting the assumptions (*a*) that λ can be assigned an average value λ_1 in the temperature interval between T_l and T_c, and (*b*) that the specific heat of the fuel vapor is constant. Thus we write the following approximate expressions:

$$\lambda=\lambda_l(T/T_l) \quad \text{.... (4.15)}$$

where λ_l is the thermal conductivity of the fuel–inert gas mixture at the temperature T_l, and

$$(c_p)_F=a+bT \quad \text{.... (4.16)}$$

where *a* and *b* are suitably chosen constants. Equations 4.13, 4.15, and 4.16 lead to the result

$$4\pi r^2(\mathrm{d}T/\mathrm{d}r)=(\dot{m}_F T_l/\lambda_l T)[a(T-T_l)+(b/2)(T^2-T_l^2)+\Delta l] \quad \text{.... (4.13a)}$$

Integration of the preceding expression from r_l, T_l to r_c, T_c shows that

$$\dot{m}_F=\frac{4\pi\lambda_l r_l}{bT_l[1-(r_l/r_c)]}\left[\ln\{1+[(T_c-T_l)/\Delta l][a+(b/2)(T_c+T_l)]\}-\frac{a}{\xi}\ln\frac{(a+bT_c-\xi)(a+bT_l+\xi)}{(a+bT_c+\xi)(a+bT_l-\xi)}\right] \quad \text{.... (4.17)}$$

where

$$\xi=\{a^2-2b[\Delta l-(b/2)T_l^2-aT_l]\}^{1/2} \quad \text{.... (4.18)}$$

*The experimental determination of r_c was greatly complicated by the fact that the combustion surface was far from spherical because of severe convection currents over the droplet.

Reference to Eq. 4.17 and 4.18 shows again that $\dot{m}_F$ is determined provided r_c and T_c are known. We shall show below that both T_c and r_c can be calculated by appropriate application of Eq. 4.11 and 4.12 by utilizing the assumption that the delivery ratio of fuel to oxygen at the reaction front corresponds to the stoichiometric mixture ratio.

(*c*) *Preliminary remarks on the use of Eq. 4.11 and 4.12*—One of the objectives of the present analysis is to establish an efficient method for the utilization of the basic relations given in Eq. 4.11 and 4.12. It will be convenient to restrict the analysis to spherical shells located between r_l and $r > r_l$, or between r_c and $r > r_c$. In this case simple explicit expressions are obtained for the rate of energy transport by thermal conduction through the surface of radius r. Thus Eq. 4.11 leads to an expression of the form

$$4\pi r^2 \lambda (\mathrm{d}T/\mathrm{d}r) = \dot{m}_F (c_p)_K (\alpha + \beta T + \epsilon T^2) \qquad \text{.... (4.19)}$$

if the specific heat is a linear function of the temperature. Here the numerical values of α, β, and ϵ must be determined for each particular problem. Equation 4.12 becomes

$$4\pi r^2 \rho \mathrm{D}_K (\mathrm{d}Y_K/\mathrm{d}r) = \dot{m}_F (Y_K - \gamma'_K) \qquad \text{.... (4.20)}$$

where

$$\gamma_K' = \dot{m}_K / \dot{m}_F \qquad \text{.... (4.21)}$$

In the use of Eq. 4.20 and 4.21, care must be taken to employ a positive value for γ_K' if mass flow occurs in the same direction as the fuel transport, and to use a negative value for γ_K' if mass flow occurs in the direction opposite to the direction of fuel transport.

It is evident by reference to Eq. 4.19 and 4.20 that we can eliminate the radial distance as independent variable and write

$$\frac{\mathrm{d}Y_K}{Y_K - \gamma_K'} = \chi_K \frac{\mathrm{d}T}{\alpha + \beta T + \epsilon T^2} \qquad \text{.... (4.22)}$$

where the dimensionless parameter χ_K, which is not a sensitive function of pressure and temperature, and which is assumed to be independent of Y_K, is defined by the relation

$$\chi_K = \lambda / \rho \mathrm{D}_K (c_p)_K \qquad \text{.... (4.23)}$$

A mean value is used for $(c_p)_K$ whereas λ, ρ and D_K are computed at any conveniently chosen temperature. Integration of Eq. 4.22 between $Y_O = 0$ at $r = r_c$ and $Y_O = Y_{O,o}$ at $r = \infty$, corresponding to T_c and T_o, respectively, leads directly to the value of T_c for specified values of T_o and $Y_{O,o}$.* Similarly, integration between $Y_F = Y_{F,l}$ at $r = r_l$,

* The same result is obtained if we integrate Eq. 4.22 from $Y_I = 1$ at $r = r_c$, $T = T_c$ to $Y_I = Y_{I,o} = 1 - Y_{O,o}$ at $r = \infty$, $T = T_o$.

$T=T_l$ and $Y_F=0$ at $r=r_c$, $T=T_c$, gives an explicit approximate expression for $Y_{F,l}=1-Y_I$.*

In order to obtain the value of r_c we can utilize Eq. 4.19 or Eq. 4.20. Equation 4.19 can be integrated directly between r_c, T_c and ∞, T_o, after expressing λ as a linear function of T. Introduction of the known relation for $\dot{m}_F$ into the resulting expression leads to an explicit relation for r_c. The integration of Eq. 4.20 is somewhat more involved since ρD_K is a linear function of T to the same approximation that λ is a linear function of T. Hence integration of Eq. 4.20 requires the determination of $T(r)$ prior to integration. We shall use Eq. 4.19 for the determination of r_c.

By utilizing constant average specific heats only in the region $r>r_c$, it is to be expected that reasonable estimates, commensurate in accuracy with our assumed physical model, will be obtained for T_c, r_c, and $\dot{m}_F$.

(*d*) *The reaction zone temperature* T_c—For the spherical shell between $r>r_c$ and r_c, Eq. 4.11 becomes

$$\dot{m}_F[(1+\gamma_O')(h_P)_T-\gamma_O'(h_O)_T]-\dot{m}_F[(1+\gamma_O')(h_P)_{T_c}-\gamma_O'(h_O)_{T_c}]$$
$$=4\pi r^2\lambda(dT/dr)-[4\pi r^2\lambda(dT/dr)]_{r_c} \quad .... \quad (4.24)$$

where h_P and h_O denote, respectively, the specific enthalpies of products of reaction and of oxidizer. But $-[4\pi r^2\lambda(dT/dr)]_{r_c}$ equals the total heat evolved on reaction at T_c minus the energy transported to the fuel droplet, i.e.,

$$-[4\pi r^2\lambda(dT/dr)]_{r_c}=$$
$$\dot{m}_F\{[-(1\gamma+_O')(h_P)_{T_c}+(h_F)_{T_c}+\gamma_O'(h_O)T_c]-\Delta l-[(h_F)_{T_c}-(h_F)_{T_l}]\}$$

where h_F is the specific enthalpy of the fuel vapor. Hence Eq. 4.24 becomes

$$-4\pi r^2\lambda(dT/dr)=\dot{m}_F\{q^*+\gamma_O'[(h_O)_T-(h_O)_{T^*}]$$
$$-(1+\gamma_O')[(h_P)_T-(h_P)_{T^*}]\} \quad .... \quad (4.25)$$

where

$$q^*=-(1+\gamma_O')(h_P)_{T^*}+(h_{F,l})_{T^*}+c_l(T_l-T^*)\dagger \quad .... \quad (4.26)$$

* The same result is obtained if we integrate Eq. 4.22 from $Y_{I,l}$ at $r=r_l$, $T=T_l$ to $Y_I=1$ at $r=r_c$, $T=T_c$.

† For the present approximate calculations the heat release q^* and, therefore T_c, r_c/r_l, and $\dot{m}_F$ are computed by neglecting the effect of dissociation of combustion products, fuel, and oxygen. The derived results would be expected to be roughly correct for gas mixtures leading to values of T_c well below 3000° K, i.e., for some hydrocarbon–air flames. The effect of dissociation on the calculated results can be incorporated into our present model by using an iteration procedure in which it is assumed that chemical equilibrium is established at every point. As the result of this refinement, the calculated values of T_c and of r_c/r_l are decreased by a first iteration; the temperature profile toward the oxidizer is flattened and the temperature raised because the reassociating gases act as a distributed heat source on recombination. The diffusive flow of oxygen inward is then increased, thereby leading to a further decrease of r_c/r_l. Rough calculations show that the net effect of dissociation on the calculated values of $\dot{m}_F$ for benzene–air flames is probably less than 10 per cent although both T_c and r_c/r_l are decreased appreciably.

Here T^* is a standard reference temperature (usually chosen as 298·16°K) and c_l denotes a constant specific heat for the liquid fuel in the temperature range between T^* and T_l; the quantity q^* differs from the standard heat of combustion for one gram of liquid fuel through the addition of the term $c_l(T_l - T^*)$. If $(c_p)_P$ and $(c_p)_O$ are independent of the temperature, then Eq. 4.25 reduces to the relation

$$-4\pi r^2\lambda(\mathrm{d}T/\mathrm{d}r) = \dot{m}_F\{q^* + (T - T^*)[\gamma_O'(c_p)_O(1 + \gamma_O')(c_p)_P]\} \quad \text{.... (4.25a)}$$

Reference to Eq. 4.25a shows that it is of the form

$$4\pi r^2\lambda(\mathrm{d}T/\mathrm{d}r) = \dot{m}_F(c_p)_O(\alpha + \beta T) \quad \text{.... (4.25b)}$$

with

$$\alpha = -[q^*/(c_p)_O] - \beta T^* \quad \text{.... (4.27)}$$

and

$$\beta = (1 + \gamma_O')\delta_P - \gamma_O' \quad \text{.... (4.28)}$$

where $\delta_K = (c_p)_K/(c_p)_O$.

From Eq. 4.20 we can obtain the appropriate expression for the mass transfer of oxidizer,

$$4\pi r^2\rho D_O(\mathrm{d}Y_O/\mathrm{d}r) = \dot{m}_F(Y_O + \gamma_O') \quad \text{.... (4.29)}$$

where a negative sign has been used for γ_O' because the oxidizer flows in a direction opposite to that of the fuel. Here D_O is the binary diffusion coefficient of oxidizer through the oxidizer–inert gas-combustion products mixture. Division of Eq. 4.25b by Eq. 4.29 leads to the expression

$$\frac{\mathrm{d}Y_O}{Y_O + \gamma_O'} = \chi_O \frac{\mathrm{d}T}{\alpha + \beta T} \quad \text{.... (4.30)}$$

where

$$\chi_O = \lambda/(c_p)_O D_O \rho$$

is a constant. Hence integration of Eq. 4.30 between $Y_O = 0$, $T = T_c$ and $Y_O = Y_{O,\infty}$, $T = T$ leads to the following explicit relation for T_c:

$$T_c = \frac{\beta T_\infty - \alpha\{[1 + (Y_{O,\infty}/\gamma_O')]^{(\beta/\chi_O)} - 1\}}{\beta[1 + (Y_{O,\infty}/\gamma_O')]^{(\beta/\chi_O)}} \quad \text{.... (4.31)}$$

It is clear that an explicit expression for T_c can be obtained also, without difficulty, if $(c_p)_P$ and $(c_p)_O$ are linear functions of the temperature. In this case ϵ in Eq. 4.19 does not equal zero. The results of introduction of this added refinement will not be given here.

(*e*) *The weight fraction profile of fuel vapor*—It is evident from the formulation of the present problem that Y_F cannot equal unity at the droplet surface. For this reason it is of interest to estimate Y_F at r_l approximately.

From Eq. 4.13a and Eq. 4.20, written in terms of the fuel, it follows that

$$\frac{dY_F}{Y_F - 1} = \frac{\lambda}{\rho D_F} \frac{dT}{(b/2)T^2 + aT + [\Delta l - aT_l - (b/2)T_l^2]} \quad \text{.... (4.32)}$$

where $\lambda/\rho D_F$ is independent of temperature and is assumed to be independent also of Y_F. Integration of Eq. 4.32 between $Y_F = Y_{F,}$ at $T = T_l$ and $Y_F = 0$ at $T = T_c$ leads to the result

$$Y_{F,l} = 1 - \left[\frac{(a + bT_c - \xi)(a + bT_l + \xi)}{(a + bT_c + \xi)(a + bT_l - \xi)}\right]^{-(\lambda/\rho D_F \xi)} \quad \text{.... (4.33)}$$

where ξ has been defined in Eq. 4.18.

(*f*) *Determination of the combustion radius*—Equation 4.25b, which was derived on the assumption that the specific heats of oxidizer and inert gas are constant for $r > r_c$, may be used directly for the determination of r_c. After replacing λ by $\lambda_l\,(T/T_l)$ and integrating from r_c, T_c to ∞, T_o, the following relation is obtained:

$$\frac{1}{r_c} = \frac{4\pi\lambda_l}{\dot{m}_F (c_p)_O T_l}\left[\frac{1}{\beta}(T_o - T_c) - \frac{\alpha}{\beta^2}\ln\frac{\alpha + \beta T_o}{\alpha + \beta T_c}\right] \quad \text{.... (4.34)}$$

where α and β are defined in Eq. 4.26 and 4.27, respectively.

From Eq. 4.17 and 4.34 we can now obtain an explicit expression for r_c/r_l. Thus we may write Eq. 4.17 in the form

$$\dot{m}_F = \frac{4\pi\lambda_l r_l}{bT_l[1 - (r_l/r_c)]}\Phi \quad \text{.... (4.17a)}$$

where

$$\Phi = \ln\{1 + [(T_c - T_l)/\Delta l][a + (b/2)(T_c + T_l)]\} - \frac{a}{\xi}\ln\frac{(a + bT_c - \xi)(a + bT_l + \xi)}{(a + bT_c + \xi)(a + bT_l - \xi)} \quad \text{.... (4.35)}$$

From Eq. 4.34 and 4.17a it is seen that

$$\frac{r_c}{r_l} = 1 + \frac{(c_p)_O \Phi}{b}\left[\frac{1}{\beta}(T_o - T_c) - \frac{\alpha}{\beta^2}\ln\frac{\alpha + \beta T_o}{\alpha + \beta T_c}\right]^{-1} \quad \text{.... (4.36)}$$

Reference to Eq. 4.36 shows the interesting result, which is in accord with some of the experimental observations, that r_c/r_l is a constant for fixed values of the physico-chemical parameters. Hence Eq. 4.17a shows that $\dot{m}_F$ is a linear function of r_l.

The linear functional relation between $\dot{m}_F$ and r_l has been used by Godsave[11,12] and others to obtain the following expression for the variation of droplet diameter with time:

$$d^2 = d_o^2 - K't \quad \text{.... (4.37)}$$

Here d is the droplet diameter at time t, d_o is the initial droplet diameter, and the evaporation constant K' is defined by the relation

$$K' = 2\dot{m}_F/\pi r_l \rho_l \quad \text{.... (4.38)}$$

Since K' is independent of r_l, it is a convenient parameter for comparing burning rates of different fuels for arbitrary droplet sizes.

(*C*) *Comparison between calculated and observed results for the burning of single droplets of fuel*

We have obtained in the preceding Sec. 4.2*B* a complete description for the burning of single droplets of fuel in an oxidizing atmosphere according to a simplified model. It is the purpose of the present discussion to compare calculated and observed values for r_c/r_l and for $K' = 2\dot{m}_F/\pi r_l \rho_l$.

The procedure for calculating various quantities, including r_c/r_l and K', involves the following steps:

(*a*) For suitably chosen values of the physico-chemical parameters we obtain T_c from Eq. 4.31.
(*b*) The limiting weight fraction $Y_{F,l}$ is next obtained from Eq. 4.33.
(*c*) The quantity r_c/r_l is given by Eq. 4.36.
(*d*) Finally $K' = 2\dot{m}_F/\pi r_l \rho_l$ is calculated either from Eq. 4.17 or from Eq. 4.17a.

For the sake of completeness we have determined also the T versus r and Y_K versus r profiles for the burning of a benzene droplet in air if $T_0 = 300°K$, $r_l = 0.005$ cm. The results of these calculations have been considered previously and are given in *Fig. 4.3a* to *4.3d.*

Calculations have been carried out for the burning of benzene, ethyl alcohol, ethyl benzene, *n*-heptane, and toluene in air, as well as for the effect of oxygen concentration on the burning rates of various fuels.*

(*a*) *Comparison of calculated and observed evaporation constants*—Calculated and observed evaporation constants for burning in air are contrasted in *Table 4.1.* Reference to *Table 4.1* shows satisfactory agreement between calculated and observed values of K' (and hence of $\dot{m}_F$). The results suggest that the physical model upon which the present analysis of burning of fuel drops is based represents a useful first approximation for the compounds considered. However, there are serious doubts that the basic physical assumptions involved in the model are applicable, for example, to the burning of an aniline droplet in nitrogen dioxide or in nitric acid vapors.

Table 4.1 Comparison of calculated and observed values for the evaporation constant K′ for burning in air

Compound	*Observed Value of K′ (cm²/sec)*	*Calculated Value of K′ (cm²/sec)*
Benzene	0·0097	0·0100
Ethyl Alcohol	0·0081	0·0079
Ethyl Benzene	0·0086	0·0085
n-Heptane	0·0097	0·0086
Toluene	0·0076†	0·0087

† Based on experimental measurements carried out by Goldsmith and Perkins.[18]

* Theoretical calculations on the evaporation rate of pure compounds into still air can be carried out by replacing T_c and T_l in Eq. 4.14 by the known ambient and droplet temperatures, respectively. The results obtained for water droplets, on the assumption that $1/r_c \ll 1/r_l$, are in very satisfactory agreement with empirically determined values.

The effect of oxygen concentration on mass burning rate of fuel droplets has recently been investigated experimentally.[18] A comparison between calculated and observed results is shown in *Fig. 4.4* and

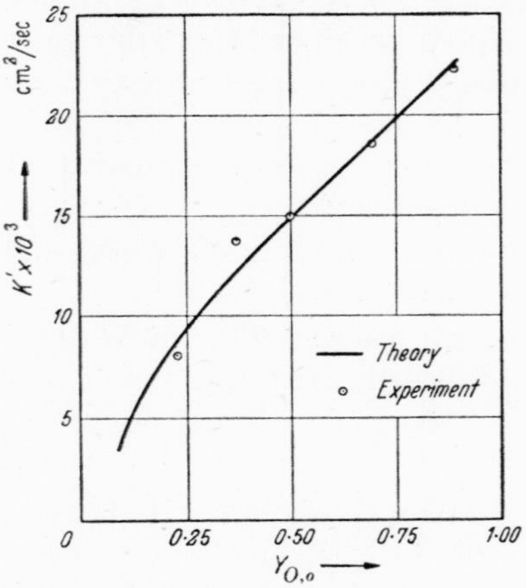

Fig. 4.4. Comparison of theoretical and experimental values for the evaporation constant, K′, for ethyl alcohol burning in various oxygen–nitrogen mixtures

Fig. 4.5 for ethyl alcohol and *n*-pentane, respectively. Reference to *Fig. 4.4* and *4.5* again shows surprisingly good agreement between calculated and observed experimental results.[18]

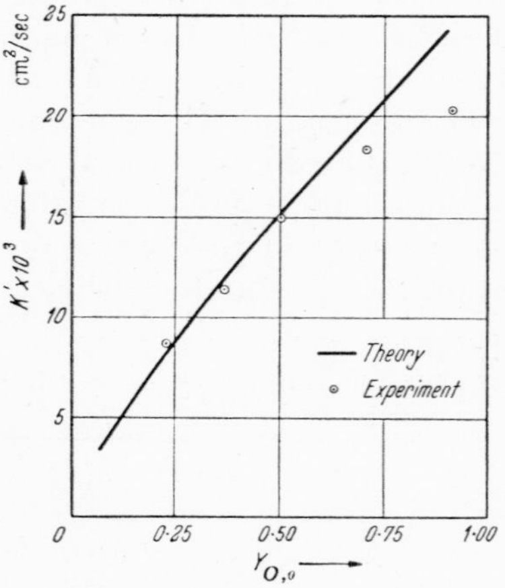

Fig. 4.5. Comparison of theoretical and experimental values for the evaporation constant, K′, for n-*heptane burning in various oxygen–nitrogen mixtures*

(*b*) *Comparison of observed and calculated values of* r_c/r_l—The theoretical analysis is based on the assumption that a spherical reaction surface surrounds the burning droplet. On the other hand, photographs of burning droplets indicate that the luminous region is of the form shown in *Fig. 4.6.* Godsave measured the diameter of the sphere corresponding to the dotted circle in *Fig. 4.6* and stated that the ratio of this diameter to the droplet diameter is a constant, characteristic for the fuel, when burning in air.

The values of r_c/r_l calculated from Eq. 4.36 are appreciably larger than the observed data. There are several obvious reasons for this observed discrepancy. Thus reference to *Fig. 4.6* shows that the 'still' droplet was actually subjected to strong convection currents during burning; the value of r_c/r_l for a spherical surface with area equivalent to the area of the observed luminous zone is roughly double that of Godsave's tabulated values. Furthermore, it is not evident that the reaction surface in our idealized model should, in fact, be identified with the region of maximum luminosity. The surface for maximum

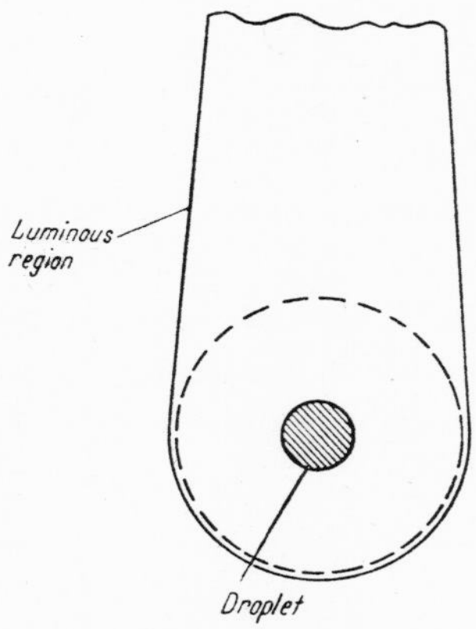

Fig. 4.6. Schematic diagram of flame front surrounding a burning droplet

temperature gradients, as determined from schlieren photographs,[12] corresponds to somewhat larger 'observed' values of r_c/r_l than the surface of maximum luminosity.

The discrepancies between calculated and 'measured' values of r_c/r_l emphasize also the need for refinement in the theoretical description of the burning process. Thus it is apparent that the introduction of a spherical reaction shell of finite thickness will lead to lower values of T_c and also to lower effective values of r_c/r_l; a similar effect is produced also if proper allowance is made for dissociation by assuming that chemical equilibrium is established at every point. Presumably the changes in T_c and in r_c/r_l will largely compensate for each other in the calculation of K' or $\dot{m}_F$, thereby accounting for the satisfactory agreement between calculated and observed values of $\dot{m}_F$.

In conclusion it seems appropriate to note that some experimental evidence exists which is not in accord with the idea that r_c/r_l is constant.

Thus HALL and DIEDERICHSEN[19] state that their studies of the burning of single drops of fuel suggest that the distance between the flame front and the drop surface remains constant.

(*c*) *Effect of pressure on the burning process*—The results of the present simplified analysis indicate that the only dependence of the burning rate on pressure occurs through the variation of the boiling points and latent heats of evaporation with pressure. The values of T_c and r_c/r_l are essentially independent of pressure. The results of Hall and Diederichsen show that the burning rate is roughly proportional to the one-fourth power of the pressure.[19] Although the present analysis does not lead to this simple functional relation, detailed calculations show that the burning rates, as predicted by theory, increase with pressure slightly, primarily because of a decrease of latent heat of evaporation at the higher boiling temperatures associated with increased pressure. Again it is clear that a quantitative description of the dependence of K' or $\dot{m}_F$ on pressure requires extension of the present analysis in several respects. Thus chemical reaction rates are sensitive functions of the pressure (for a complicated process, an overall dependence of the reaction rate on the square of the pressure is not unreasonable) and, therefore, a very weak dependence of $\dot{m}_F$ on reaction rates could account for the observed variation of $\dot{m}_F$ with pressure. Furthermore, the effects of radiant heat transfer to the droplet surface, which have been neglected in the present study, increase rapidly with pressure and could account for a weak dependence of $\dot{m}_F$ on pressure. Finally, free convection currents can be shown to lead, approximately, to a variation of $\dot{m}_F$ with the fourth root of the pressure since the overall heat transfer coefficient for free convection depends on the fourth root of the pressure,[20] and $\dot{m}_F$ is directly proportional to the heat transfer to the droplet surface. A study of free convection effects also suggests that the radius of the combustion surface varies inversely as the square root of the pressure, in accord with the experimental results of Hall and Diederichsen.[19]

(*d*) *Residue formation in the burning of aromatic fuels*—For oxygen weight fractions exceeding 23 per cent, formation of residue was observed during the burning of benzene and toluene.[18] The residue remaining on the filament at the conclusion of combustion was of a dry, brittle, consistency. The formation of carbon in heterogeneous combustion of aromatic hydrocarbon fuels has been observed by other investigators and merits additional quantitative study. Because of residue formation during the burning of benzene and toluene, it is not possible to determine accurately the burning rates of these fuels. The shroudlike formation of residue causes considerable distortion of the drop, and often surrounds and obscures the drop of fuel.

Carbon formation during the heterogeneous combustion of aromatic fuels, but not during the burning of aliphatic compounds, re-emphasizes the importance of chemical reaction rates, which have been neglected in the discussion of the diffusion model for droplet burning. According to one of the modern theories for carbon formation during burning,[21] acetylene production is an essential intermediate step. One might therefore argue that the greater tendency of aromatic fuels to form carbonaceous residues is related to the known ease with which these compounds form acetylene. This qualitative suggestion does not offer a satisfactory explanation for the dependence of residue formation on oxygen concentration. In order to describe quantitatively the formation of carbon in heterogeneous combustion, it is clearly necessary to allow for the interdependence of chemical reaction rates, mass transport by concentration and thermal diffusion, and energy transport by thermal conduction. The analysis of homogeneous, as well as of heterogeneous, diffusion flames, with proper allowance for the detailed chemical processes occurring in the flame front, is one of the soluble fundamental problems in the dynamics of reacting fluids.

REFERENCES

1 LANGMUIR, I., *J. Amer. chem. Soc.* 38 (1916) 2221

2 *See* e.g., EMMETT, P. H. (ed.), *Catalysis, Vol. 1 Fundamental Principles* (Pt 1), Reinhold Publ. Corpn., New York, 1954

3 *See* reference 2, Chapter 4 "Kinetic Laws in Surface Catalysis" and Chapter 5 "Absolute Rates of Surface Reactions" (K. J. LAIDLER)

4 SEMENOFF, N., *Chemical Kinetics and Chain Reactions*, Oxford Univ. Pr., New York, 1935

5 KASSEL, L. S., and STORCH, H. H., *J. Amer. chem. Soc.* 57 (1935) 672

6 LEWIS, B., and VON ELBE, G., *Combustion, Flames, and Explosions of Gases*, pp. 14–26, Academic Pr. Inc., New York, 1951

7 HINSHELWOOD, C. N., *Proc. roy. Soc.* A 188 (1946) 1

8 LAIDLER, K. J., *Chemical Kinetics*, Chapter 11, McGraw-Hill Book Co., New York, 1950

9 *See* e.g., (*a*) GODSAVE, G. A. E., "The Combustion of Drops in a Fuel Spray" *Nat. Gas Turb. Establ. (England), Memor.* No. M 95, 1950
(*b*) MIESSE, C. C., "One-dimensional Velocity Variation of a Burning Droplet", Heat Transfer and Fluid Mechanics Inst., Los Angeles, 1953
(*c*) MULLINS, B. P., "Studies on the Spontaneous Ignition of Fuels injected in a Hot Air Stream", Pt 1, *Nat. Gas Turb. Establ. (England)*, Rep. No. R 89, 1951; Pt II, *ibid.*, No. R 90, 1951

10 GODSAVE, G. A. E., "The Burning of Single Drops of Fuel: Pt I Temperature Distribution and Heat Transfer in the Pre-flame Region", *ibid.*, No. R 66, 1950

11 —, *ibid.*, "Pt II, Experimental Results", *ibid.*, No. R 87, 1951

12 —, *ibid.*, "Pt III, Comparison of Experimental and Theoretical Burning Rates and Discussion of the Mechanism of the Combustion Process", *ibid.*, No. R 88, 1952

13 TOPPS, J. E. C., *J. Inst. Petrol.* 37 (1951) 535

[14] Spalding, D. B., *Fuel* 29 (1950) 2, 25; AGARD Combustion Colloquium, *Selected Combustion Problems—Fundamentals and Aeronautical Applications*, "Combustion of a Single Droplet and of a Fuel Spray", pp. 340–351, Butterworths, London, 1954

[15] Tanasawa, Y., and Kobayashi, K., "On the Evaporation Velocity of a Liquid Droplet in a High-Temperature Gas", *Technol. Rep. Tohoku Univ.* 14 (1950) No. 2

Kumagai, S., and Isoda, H., *Science of Machine* 4 (1952) 337

Kumagai, S., and Kimura, A., *Science of Machine* 3 (1951) 431

[16] Penner, S. S., *J. Amer. Rocket Soc.* 23 (1953) 85

[17] Hartwig, F. W., *T.c.* 242

[18] Perkins, C. K., A.E. Thesis, California Inst. of Technology, June 1954

Goldsmith, M., and Perkins, C. K., *Tech. Rep.* No. 4, *Contract DA*-495-*Ord.*-446, *Off. Ordnance Res., U.S. Army,* California Inst. of Technology, Pasadena, May 1954

[19] Hall, A. R., and Diederichsen, J., "An Experimental Study of the Burning of Single Drops of Fuel in Air at Pressures up to Twenty Atmospheres", *4th (Int.) Symp. Combust.* pp. 837–46, Williams and Wilkins Co., Baltimore, 1953

[20] McAdams, W. H., *Heat Transmission* pp. 237–51, McGraw-Hill Book Co., New York, 1942

[21] Porter, G., "Carbon Formation in the Combustion Wave", *4th (Int.) Symp. Combust.* pp. 248–52, Williams and Wilkins Co., Baltimore, 1953

NAME INDEX

SUBJECT INDEX